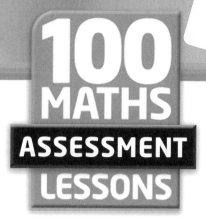

SCHOLASTIC

C000116160

100 MATHS ASSESSMENT LESSONS

TERMS AND CONDITIONS

IMPORTANT – PERMITTED USE AND WARNINGS – READ CAREFULLY BEFORE USING

Licence

YEAR 1

Scottish Primary 2

Minimum specification:
- PC or Mac with a CD-ROM drive and 512 Mb RAM (recommended)
- Windows 98SE or above/Mac OSX.4 or above
- Recommended minimum processor speed: 1 GHz

For all technical support queries, please phone Scholastic Customer Services on 0845 603 9091.

Ann Montague-Smith

CREDITS

Author
Ann Montague-Smith

Series Consultant
Ann Montague-Smith

Development Editor
Mary Nathan

Editor
Christine Vaughan

Assistant Editors
Gemma Smith and
Margaret Eaton

Series Designers
Joy Monkhouse, Micky Pledge
and Melissa Leeke

Designer
Quadrum Publishing Solutions

Illustrations
Garry Davies, Baz Rowell/
Beehive Illustrations

CD-ROM development
CD-ROM developed in
association with Vivid
Interactive

Additional material
Transitional tests written by
Joan Nield and Lesley Fletcher

Mixed Sources
Product group from well-managed
forests and other controlled sources
www.fsc.org Cert no. TT-COC-002769
© 1996 Forest Stewardship Council

FSC

ACKNOWLEDGEMENTS

Extracts from the Primary National Strategy's *Primary Framework for Mathematics* (2006) www.standards.dfes.gov.uk/primaryframework and the Interactive Teaching Programs originally developed for the National Numeracy Strategy © Crown copyright. Reproduced under the terms of the Click Use Licence.

Every effort has been made to trace copyright holders for the works reproduced in this book, and the publishers apologise for any inadvertent omissions.

Published by Scholastic Ltd
Villiers House
Clarendon Avenue
Leamington Spa
Warwickshire CV32 5PR

www.scholastic.co.uk

Designed using Adobe InDesign.

Printed by Bell and Bain Ltd, Glasgow

1 2 3 4 5 6 7 8 9   9 0 1 2 3 4 5 6 7 8

Text © 2009 Ann Montague-Smith

© 2009 Scholastic Ltd

British Library Cataloguing-in-Publication Data
A catalogue record for this book is available from the British Library.

ISBN 978-1407-10183-5

The rights of the author of this work have been asserted by her in accordance with the Copyright, Designs and Patents Act 1988.

Contents

100 Maths Assessment Lessons

About the series

100 Maths Assessment Lessons is designed to provide assessment opportunities for all children. Linked to the renewed *Primary Framework for Mathematics*, it also supports the implementation of the new *Assessing Pupil's Progress* (APP) guidelines by linking the new APP assessment focuses to the PNS Framework objectives. Each title in the series also provides single-level tests that can be used at the end of a year, or at any point throughout the year, to provide a summary of where, in relation to national standards, learners are at a given point in time. By using the titles in this series, a teacher or school can be sure that they are covering the mathematics curriculum and obtaining relevant data about their children's achievements.

About assessment

100 Maths Assessment Lessons provides a wide range of opportunities for teachers and children to assess progress. There are three different types of assessment identified by the APP guidelines:

Day to day

Day-to-day assessment is an integral and essential part of effective learning and teaching. Teachers and children continually reflect on how learning is progressing, see where improvements can be made and identify the next steps to take. Strategies that should be part of everyday learning and teaching include:
● sharing and talking about learning objectives, learning outcomes and success criteria with children
● observing and listening to gather intelligence
● planning for group talk, peer assessment and self-assessment to help children develop as independent learners.

Periodic assessment

The purpose of periodic assessment is to give an overview of progress and provide diagnostic information about the progress of individual children, linked to national standards. It is intended to be used at regular (half-termly or termly) intervals to provide an overview of performance based on a wide range of evidence. Periodic assessment should be used to:
● make a periodic review of progress and attainment across a whole task
● identify gaps in experience and inform planning
● help learners know and recognise the standards they are aiming for
● involve both learner and teacher in reviewing and reflecting on evidence.

Transitional assessment

Transitional assessment should be used at points of transition which might be from year to year, school to school or level to level. The pupils' progress data from day-to-day assessment and periodic assessment will support the teacher in making decisions about how pupils are likely to perform in transitional assessments. The key characteristics of transitional assessment are:
● it brings together evidence, including tests, to reach a view of attainment

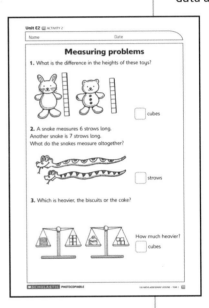

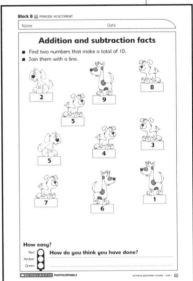

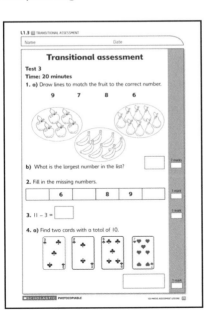

- it is externally validated and externally communicated
- it is set within the framework of national standards.

For a complete list of strategies for day-to-day assessment and further information about periodic and transitional assessment, visit the National Strategies website (**http://nationalstrategies.standards.dcsf.gov.uk**).

About this book

This book is set out in the five blocks that form the renewed *Primary Framework for Mathematics*. Each block consists of three units, with each unit containing:
- an overview of the work covered in the unit, including the objectives, assessment focuses and learning outcomes for each activity (end-of-year objectives are denoted in bold text)
- day-to-day assessment activities based upon the assessment for learning and children's learning outcomes for each objective within a unit (note that the using and applying objectives are either incorporated into other assessments, or assessed on their own, depending upon the content and context of the unit)
- periodic assessment activities based on the end-of-year objectives within each unit.

Assessment activities

Each activity contains:
- details of children's expected prior learning before the activity is used
- the relevant objective(s) and vocabulary that children are expected to know
- description of the activity for the teacher or learning support assistant
- group, paired or individual work for the children. Where adult intervention is required, this is explained. Most of the activities include the use of an activity sheet or interactive activity from the CD-ROM
- clear differentiation, to support less confident learners in the group or to extend the learning for the more confident learners
- common misconceptions and how to remediate these
- probing questions to ask the children
- next steps: these are differentiated to help teachers decide how to help children who need further support. Suggestions for further work and references to related Framework units or blocks are given to support or extend the children.

What's on the CD-ROM?

Each CD-ROM contains a wealth of resources. These include:
- **worksheets** with answers, where appropriate, that can be toggled by clicking on the 'show' or 'hide' buttons at the bottom of the screen
- **transitional assessments:** year-appropriate single-level tests, oral tests, mark schemes and instructions
- **general resource sheets** (for example, number grids) designed to support a number of lessons
- **interactive activities:** for individuals or small groups, with in-built marking to assess specific objectives

- **Interactive Teaching Programs:** specific ITPs, originally developed for the National Numeracy Strategy
- **whiteboard tools:** a set of tools (including a pen, highlighter and eraser) that can be used to annotate activity sheets for whole-class lessons. These tools will work on any interactive whiteboard
- **display pages:** some activities require a problem or investigation to be shown to the whole class on an interactive whiteboard. The whiteboard tools can also be used with these images to annotate them as necessary
- **editable planning grids** (in Word format) are available to help teachers integrate the lessons into their planning.

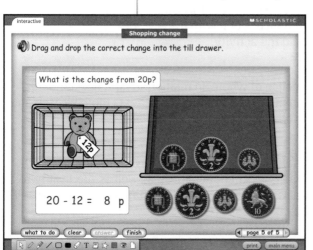

How to use the CD-ROM

System requirements
Minimum specification:
- PC or Mac with a CD-ROM drive and 512 Mb RAM (recommended)
- Windows 98SE or above/Mac OS X.4 or above
- Recommended minimum processor speed: 1 GHz

Getting started
The *100 Maths Assessment Lessons* CD-ROM should auto run when inserted into your CD drive. If it does not, browse to your CD drive to view the contents of the CD-ROM and click on the *100 Maths Assessment Lessons* icon.

From the start-up screen you will find four options: select **Credits** to view a list of acknowledgements. Click on **Register** to register the product in order to receive product updates and special offers. Click on **How to use this CD-ROM** to access support notes for using the CD-ROM. Finally, if you agree to the terms and conditions, select **Start** to move to the main menu.

For all technical support queries, contact Scholastic Customer Services help desk on 0845 6039091.

How to use the materials
The materials contained in the book and on the CD-ROM can be used with one child, a group, or in a whole-class activity. Decide who is ready to be assessed from the daily work that the children complete and from your observations. The CD-ROM allows users to search for resources by block, unit or lesson. Users can also search by Framework objective, assessment focus or by resource type (for example, worksheet, interactive resource, display page or ITP).

Day-to-day assessments
These should be used to support learning. They can be used during a lesson, when you judge that children are ready for an assessment activity. The materials can also be used weekly or after a unit of work has been completed.

Periodic assessments
These can be used with a group of children rather than with the whole class. This could be at the end of a unit of work (for example, at the end of a half-term or term). Decide who is ready to be assessed using the outcomes of the day-to-day assessment activities and your observations of children's performance.

Self-assessment
A self-assessment sheet is provided for you and the children to complete. It can be used where there is no activity sheet, so that there is evidence of the children's confidence in what they have learned and how well they can use that learning. There are 'traffic lights' at the bottom of the sheet that children can shade to show their confidence: red for 'need help'; orange for 'having some understanding'; green for 'go!' (ie the child feels confident with his/her learning).

All the activity sheets also have the traffic light system for the children to record their level of confidence, along with a space for them to write about how easy/hard they found the activity.

Transitional tests
These tests provide evidence of where, in relation to national standards, children are at a given point in time. Photocopiable tests (both written and oral), mark schemes and answer sheets are all available on the CD-ROM.

Class PET
A whole-school version of *100 Maths Assessment Lessons* is available with an expanded range of digital assessment activities, as well as the facility to report, record and track pupil's work. For further information visit the Class PET website, **www.scholastic.co.uk/classpet**.

BLOCK A

Counting, partitioning and calculating

Expected prior learning
Check that children can already:
- solve practical problems involving counting, including counting on, measuring, comparing, ordering, adding, subtracting or partitioning objects
- say and use the number names in order in familiar contexts and recognise numerals 1 to 9
- know that numbers identify how many objects are in a set and match sets of objects to numerals
- count aloud in ones, twos, fives or tens
- find one more or one less than a number from 1 to 10
- select two groups of objects to make a given total of objects
- relate addition to combining two groups of objects and subtraction to 'taking away'.

Objectives overview
The text in this diagram identifies the focus of mathematics learning within the block.

Key aspects of learning
- Problem solving
- Social skills
- Communication

Comparing, ordering, reading and writing numbers from 0 to at least 20

Using knowledge of place value to record numbers on tracks and lines

Learning and counting at least 20 objects

Recognising that when objects are rearranged the number is the same

Early addition and related language and symbols including equals (=) sign

BLOCK A: Counting, partitioning and calculating

Learning number names

Counting forwards and backwards from 0 to 20, then beyond

Place value

Solving problems involving counting, adding and subtracting

Explaining methods and reasoning using related vocabulary

Unit 1 ▨ Counting, partitioning and calculating

Introduction
In this unit children should be encouraged to discuss the mathematics, use the relevant vocabulary and ask and answer questions. Encourage them to explain how they solved problems, including the choices they had and the decisions they made. Mini worlds and home-area play can be used to practise counting, addition and subtraction. Encourage children to count in different contexts and to combine sets by counting up from the larger number.

Framework objectives	Assessment focuses		Success criteria for Year 1	Learning outcomes
	Foundation stage profile scale point	Level 1		
① Counting puzzle				
Describe ways of solving puzzles and problems, explaining choices and decisions orally or using pictures	NLC 8 Uses developing mathematical ideas and methods to solve practical problems	• discuss their work	• can solve problems by counting • can talk about how the problem was solved	*I can talk about how I solve problems using counting.*
Count reliably at least 20 objects, recognising that when rearranged the number of objects stays the same; estimate a number of objects that can be checked by counting	NLC 6 Counts reliably up to 10 everyday objects	• count up to 10 objects, e.g. • estimate and check a number	• counts efficiently each member of a set just once, and knows that the last number said represents the set total • can re-count the set in a different order, and knows that the total is still the same • moves the set of objects around, and knows that the total is still the same	*I can count up to 20 objects.* *I know that the number of objects does not change even if I move the objects around.*
② How many?				
Compare and order numbers, using the related vocabulary; use the equals (=) sign	C 3 Finds one more or one less from a group of up to five objects C 7 Finds one more or one less than a number from 1 to 10	• order numbers to 10 • say what number comes next, is one more/less	• can compare two numbers and recognise the larger number • can demonstrate this knowledge using a number track or line	*I can compare numbers up to 20 and say which number is bigger.*
③ Show me numbers				
Read and write numerals from 0 to 20, then beyond; use knowledge of place value to position these numbers on a number track and number line	NLC 5 Recognises numerals 1 to 9 NLC 9 Recognises, counts, orders, writes and uses numbers up to 20	• read, write numbers to 10 • perhaps with some reversal	• can write numbers to 20 correctly • can read numbers to 20 on a number track	*I know how to write numbers up to 20.* *I can read numbers on a number track.*

Unit 1   Counting, partitioning and calculating

Framework objectives	Assessment focuses		Success criteria for Year 1	Learning outcomes
	Foundation stage profile scale point	Level 1		
④ What's more, what's less?				
Say the number that is 1 more or less than any given number, and 10 more or less for multiples of 10	C 3 Finds one more or one less from a group of up to five objects C 7 Finds one more or one less than a number from 1 to 10	• order numbers to 10 • say what number comes next, is one more/less	• can count on or back 1 to find the number that is one more/less than any number to 20 • may be beginning to recognise, without counting, the one more/less number	*I can work out the number that is one more or one less than numbers up to 20.*
⑤ Adding				
Relate addition to counting on; recognise that addition can be done in any order; use practical and informal written methods to support the addition of a one-digit number or a multiple of 10 to a one-digit or two-digit number	C 4 Relates addition by combining two groups C 5 Relates subtraction to taking away	• add numbers of objects to 10 • begin to add by counting on from the number of objects in the first set	• can count on from one number to find an addition total • is beginning to recognise that it is easier to count on from the larger number to find an addition	*I can add two one-digit numbers.*
⑥ How many are left?				
Understand subtraction as 'take away' and find a 'difference' by counting up; use practical and informal written methods to support the subtraction of a one-digit number from a one-digit or two-digit number and a multiple of 10 from a two-digit number	C 5 Relates subtraction to taking away	• subtract numbers of objects to 10	• can count out a given number of objects, then take away the required number and count what is left	*I can use objects to take away a small number from any number up to 20.*
⑦ Adding and subtracting				
Use the vocabulary related to addition and subtraction and symbols to describe and record addition and subtraction number sentences	C 6 In practical activities and discussion, begins to use the vocabulary involved in adding and subtracting	• record their work, e.g. • record their work with objects, pictures or diagrams • begin to use the symbols '+' and '=' to record additions	• can make an addition or subtraction sentence to describe a practical addition or subtraction • can write an addition or subtraction sentence using +, − and = • can talk about the addition or subtraction	*I can talk about adding/ subtracting. I can record additions/ subtractions.*

BLOCK A

Activity ①

Prior learning

Children can talk about how they solve problems using counting. They can count up to 20 objects. They know that the number of objects does not change even if they move the objects around.

Framework objectives
- Describe ways of solving puzzles and problems, explaining choices and decisions orally or using pictures
- Count reliably at least 20 objects, recognising that when rearranged the number of objects stays the same; estimate a number of objects that can be checked by counting

Vocabulary
pattern, answer, explain, show me, read, write, record, count, compare, order, counting numbers up to 20

Resources
Resource sheet: Self-assessment
Classroom resources: counting objects (such as cubes)

① Counting puzzle

Say a number. Ask the children in pairs to take turns to count out that number of objects (for example, cubes). Their partner checks the count, counting the cubes in a different order. Check that the children are counting accurately. Pose a problem: *I have eight cubes. I need to give one to each of you. How many more do I need?* Invite the children to discuss the problem in pairs and then to explain their solution. Decide whether to use the self-assessment sheet for the children to record their achievements and what they need to do next. They can draw a set of items and write how many there are, to show that they can count accurately.

Teacher support
Less confident learners: Limit the size of the count to up to 5, then to 10, to 12, and so on over time.
More confident learners: If children are confident with counting out objects up to 20, extend the count to 25, then 30.

Common misconception
Children do not match the count to the item that they are counting.
Provide some counting items. Ask children to count out aloud, say, five items. Watch to see whether the child coordinates the 'touch, say and move' of each item. If they do not, show them how to do this, and practise together. Repeat for other counts until children are confident in counting out a quantity.

Probing questions
- How do you know you have that number? How could you check your answer?
- How do you know you have counted every cube?

Next steps
Support: Provide further opportunities for counting, including counting as a chant, saying or singing counting rhymes, counting items in mini-world play such as the garage, house, and so on. See also Foundation Stage Overview of Learning 1.
Extension: Where children count confidently to 20, extend the count to over 20 and to counting out more objects. Set challenges such as: *How many pencils do I need so that everybody has one?* See also Year 1 Block B Unit 1 and Block D Unit 1.

BLOCK A

Activity ②

Prior learning
Children can compare numbers up to 20 and say which number is bigger.

Framework objective
Compare and order numbers, using the related vocabulary; use the equals (=) sign

Vocabulary
pattern, answer, explain, show me, read, write, record, count, compare, order

Resources
Worksheet: How many?
Classroom resources: counting items (such as cubes)

② How many?

Provide each pair of children with about 30 counting items. Ask them to take turns to count out some items and to say how many there are. Their partner makes a larger group of items by counting out. Ask the children to compare their sets and to check that the second set is larger. Repeat several times. Check that they count out accurately and that the second set counted is always larger than the first. Now provide the worksheet 'How many?'. This asks the children to place some pairs of numbers on a number track and to circle the larger number in each case.

Teacher support
Less confident learners: Limit the size of the numbers to compare to up to 10, at first.
More confident learners: Challenge these children to compare larger numbers beyond 20, and to say which is larger.

Common misconception
Children do not know the order of numbers and so cannot compare two numbers and say which is larger.
Chant the counting numbers together. Ask children to count from 1 and to stop when you say 'stop'. *What is the last number that you said? What will the next number in the count be? Which number is bigger?* Point to a number on a numbered track, such as 12. Ask children to point to a larger number.

Probing questions
● Would you rather have 9 pence or 15 pence? Why?
● Look at these numbers: 3, 12. Which number is bigger? Can you use objects or a number track to show how you know? What other numbers are bigger than 3 but not as big as 12?

Next steps
Support: Work at first with numbers up to 10, and then extend the range as children grow in confidence. See also Foundation Stage Overview of Learning 2.
Extension: Provide opportunities for children to identify numbers that are smaller than the given number. See also Year 1 Block A Unit 2.

BLOCK A

Activity ③

Prior learning
Children know how to write numbers up to 20. They can read numbers on a number track.

Framework objective
Read and write numerals from 0 to 20, then beyond; use knowledge of place value to position these numbers on a number track and number line

Vocabulary
read, write, record, count, compare, order

Resources
Worksheet: Show me numbers
Classroom resources: whiteboards and pens

③ Show me numbers

Explain to the children that you are going to describe a number. Ask them to write the number clearly on their whiteboards. When you say *Show me,* they hold up their boards for you to see. Check that the numbers are correct, written the correct way round and legible. *Write a number that has a straight line in it. Write another number with a straight line. Write a number that has no straight lines. Write the number that is 1 more than 8. Write the number that is between 12 and 14.* Give each child the worksheet 'Show me numbers' and ask them to write the missing numbers on the track.

Teacher support
Less confident learners: Limit the numbers to below 10. Gradually extend the range as children become more confident.
More confident learners: If children are confident with numbers to 20, ask questions such as: *Which number is between 12 and 18? Write all the numbers you can.*

Common misconception
Children do not read and/or write the numbers correctly.
Provide further experience of reading numbers. Ask children to draw numbers in the air, following your air-drawing with their whole arm. Provide opportunities to draw numbers using different media, such as in sand, with paint, or making a Plasticine number from Plasticine 'worms'. When children are confident with reading and writing numbers to 10, extend this to up to 20.

Probing questions
● Can you think of a number that has a straight line in it? Write it in the air. Do you know any more?
● Which numbers less than 20 are formed from only straight lines?

Next steps
Support: Where children are unsure about reading and writing numbers, limit the range to up to 5 or 6, then to 9 or 10. Provide opportunities for children to read numbers in storybooks and around the school, for example in displays where items can be counted and numeral cards can be matched to the count. See also Foundation Stage Overview of Learning 6.
Extension: Encourage children to find, read and copy numbers in their environment. For example, ask them to collect numbers that they see on their way home from school. See also Year 1 Block A Unit 2.

■SCHOLASTIC

Activity ④

Prior learning
Children can work out the number that is one more or one less than numbers up to 20.

Framework objective
Say the number that is 1 more or less than any given number, and 10 more or less for multiples of 10

Vocabulary
read, write, record, count, compare, order, 1 more, 1 less, 1 fewer

Resources
Resource sheets: Self-assessment, Numeral cards 0–10, Numeral cards 11-20, Numeral cards 21-30

④ What's more, what's less?

Give each pair of children a shuffled set of 1-19 numeral cards. They take turns to take the top card. The child who draws the card says the 'one more' number. The other child says the 'one less' number. They check each other's answers to make sure that they agree. As the children play this game, check that their answers are correct. *How did you work out your answers?* Ask them to choose a number and write 'one less' and 'one more' – for example, write the number 14 and they should identify 13 and 15. Repeat several times. Decide whether to use the self-assessment sheet for the children to record their achievements and what they need to do next.

Teacher support
Less confident learners: Limit the number range to up to 8, then 10, 15 and up to 20 as children become confident.
More confident learners: Ask these children to say both the 'one more' and 'one less' numbers as they play the game with a partner.

Common misconception
Children do not know the counting number order sufficiently well in order to count back 1, or on 1, in order to find one less or one more.
Provide further experience of chanting the numbers in order up to 20 from and back to 0. Stop on a number. *What is the last number that you said? So what is the next number? What is one more than 8?* Repeat. Extend to 'one less'. *What is the last number that you said? So what is the number one before 8? So what is one less than 8?*

Probing questions
● There are seven beads in this pot. I put in one more bead. How many are in the pot now? How did you know? How can you check?
● This time there are ten beads in the pot. I take out one bead. How many beads are left in the pot?

Next steps
Support: Continue with chanting the counting numbers. Stop children on, say, 12. *What is the next number that you would say? What was the number before 12? So what is 1 more than 12? What is 1 less than 12?* Repeat this frequently, as part of an oral and mental starter, until children are confident. See also Foundation Stage Overview of Learning 2.
Extension: Extend the number range to beyond 20. The children can play the same game using numeral cards to 29. See also Year 1 Block A Unit 2.

BLOCK A

Activity ⑤

Prior learning
Children can add two one-digit numbers.

Framework objective
Relate addition to counting on; recognise that addition can be done in any order; use practical and informal written methods to support the addition of a one-digit number or a multiple of 10 to a one-digit or two-digit number

Vocabulary
add, plus, makes, sum, total, altogether

Resources
Resource sheets: Self-assessment, Counting track
Classroom resources: cubes or counters

⑤ Adding

Ask the children to count out four cubes. *How many would there be if you took another two cubes? Count on in your heads.* They check by adding two cubes, counting on as they do this: *4 and 5, 6. So there are 6 altogether.* Repeat for other amounts. *How else could we work out the answer?* Discuss different methods, such as counting on fingers or counting on along a number track. Ask the children to add 3 to 5 counted out cubes. They can draw or write to show an addition. Decide whether to use the self-assessment sheet for the children to record their achievements and what they need to do next.

Teacher support
Less confident learners: Keep the numbers smaller, up to 6 in total. Once children are confident, extend the number total to up to 10.
More confident learners: Encourage these children to work just mentally, at first keeping the number total to about 8 or 9. Extend to 10 and more.

Common misconception
Children do not understand how to count on to find an addition total.
Provide a counting track and cubes. *How can we find 2 more than 3?* Make a cube tower of 2 and another of 3. Hold the 3 tower, and then count on for the 2 tower: *3 and 4, 5. So the answer is 5. What is 3 add 2?* Repeat using the counting track. Repeat for 3 + 3, 4 + 2 and so on until children are confident. Extend to counting on mentally. Some children may want to keep count using their fingers. Allow this at this point.

Probing questions
● How can you show me that 3 add 5 is 8? Can you show me using cubes? Can you put something on paper to show it? Can you use a number track?
● There are six pencils in this bag. Add three more. Without looking inside, how many are there now?

Next steps
Support: Provide further experience of adding small quantities, using a mini world such as a garage with cars, or mini people. *There are three people here. There are two more over there. How many is that altogether?* See also Foundation Stage Overview of Learning 8.
Extension: Continue to encourage children to work mentally, using counting on at this stage. Extend the number range to numbers that cross the tens barrier. See also Year 1 Block A Unit 2.

Activity ⑥

Prior learning
Children can use objects to take away a small number from any number up to 20.

Framework objective
Understand subtraction as 'take away' and find a 'difference' by counting up; use practical and informal written methods to support the subtraction of a one-digit number from a one-digit or two-digit number and a multiple of 10 from a two-digit number

Vocabulary
subtract, minus, take away, leaves

Resources
Resource sheet: Self-assessment
Classroom resources: interlocking cubes, containers (empty margarine tubs)

⑥ How many are left?

Provide each child with up to 20 cubes and a container. Ask them to make a tower from five cubes. *Marc has five bricks. He builds a tower with them. Paul takes away three bricks. How many bricks are left?* Observe how children solve the problem, and ask them to explain their method. Ask them to say a subtraction sentence: *5 take away 3 leaves 2.* Repeat, for example: *Sara has eight sweets. She eats three. How many sweets are left?* Decide whether to use the self-assessment sheet for the children to record their achievements and next steps. They can write a subtraction sentence for one of the word problems.

Teacher support
Less confident learners: Decide whether to limit the quantity of cubes to up to 6, then extend to 10 and beyond.
More confident learners: When these children are confident with subtracting practically a small quantity from up to 20, encourage children to work mentally.

Common misconception
Children do not understand how to subtract either mentally or using objects. Ask children to make a tower of four bricks. *Take away one brick. How many bricks are left? Say with me: 4 take away 1 leaves 3.* Repeat for 4 − 2 and 4 − 3. Repeat for larger quantities. When children are confident working practically, return to a small quantity such as 4. *I take away 1. How many are left?* Discuss how to work this out by counting back from 4. Repeat until children are confident with small numbers, and then extend the number range.

Probing questions
● Use cubes to work out 9 take away 4. How could you record that as a number sentence?
● Make up a 'take away'/subtraction. How do you do it?
● Pick up seven cubes. How many more do you need to make 10? How did you work it out?

Next steps
Support: Ask children subtraction questions in context, such as counting out a given number of fir cones and then removing some; counting out pencils for the table and removing some. See also Foundation Stage Overview of Learning 9.
Extension: Encourage these children to work mentally when subtracting, either by counting back from the larger number, or by counting on from the smaller number. See also Year 1 Block A Unit 2.

BLOCK A

Activity ⑦

Prior learning
Children can talk about adding/subtracting. They can record additions/subtractions.

Framework objective
Use the vocabulary related to addition and subtraction and symbols to describe and record addition and subtraction number sentences

Vocabulary
add, plus, makes, sum, total, altogether, subtract, minus, take away, leaves

Resources
Worksheet: Adding and subtracting
Resource sheet: Counting track
Classroom resources: cubes

⑦ Adding and subtracting

Provide the worksheet 'Adding and subtracting' and work with a group of up to eight children. Explain that you will read the stories on the sheet to the children. Ask them to work mentally or use cubes or number tracks to find the answer to each story. They should write an addition or subtraction sentence with the answer for the story, writing + or − between the empty boxes. Read each story at least twice. Observe how the children respond to the addition or subtraction. Check whether they work mentally or with apparatus. Ask them to explain how they worked out the answer.

Teacher support
Less confident learners: Work with smaller numbers, such as answers to up to 4.
More confident learners: Encourage these children to find the answers by working mentally.

Common misconception
Children do not understand the vocabulary of addition and subtraction.
Read the first problem. Ask children to say what sort of problem it is: adding or taking away. Ask them to explain which words tell them this. If they are still unsure, then use the same language and use cubes to demonstrate the problem. Repeat this several times for both addition and subtraction problems until children can use the vocabulary for themselves.

Probing questions
● There are five toy cars and a garage. Make number stories like these: *One car is in the garage and four cars outside, which is five altogether. 1 + 4 = 5. Five cars are in the garage. One drives away, which leaves four cars. 5 − 1 = 4.*

Next steps
Support: Encourage children to use cubes and counting tracks to help them to find the solutions to addition and subtraction questions. Then show them how to count on or back to find the solutions. See also Foundation Stage Overview of Learning 9.
Extension: Increase the number range as children become more confident. Encourage them to work mentally. See also Year 1 Block E Unit 1.

Unit 2 Counting, partitioning and calculating

Introduction
In this unit children should be encouraged to listen carefully to what you say and to follow instructions. Encourage those who are unsure to ask for help. Children should describe how they solved problems; encourage them to explain choices and decisions. They continue to estimate how many, count reliably and understand that each item should only be counted once. They develop their understanding of place value in practical situations, understanding that, for example, one ten and three units is equal to 13. They read, write and order numbers. They continue to develop their skills in addition and subtraction.

Framework objectives	Assessment focuses		Success criteria for Year 1	Learning outcomes
	Foundation stage profile scale point	Level 1		
① Estimate and count				
Count reliably at least 20 objects, recognising that when rearranged the number of objects stays the same; estimate a number of objects that can be checked by counting	NLC 6 Counts reliably up to 10 everyday objects	• count up to 10 objects, e.g. • estimate and check a number	• can make a reasonable estimate of how many are in a group of up to 20 objects • checks the quantity by counting accurately each item just once • knows that the last number said in a count represents how many there are in that set	I can estimate the number in a group of up to 20 objects. I can check the number by counting.
② Comparing and ordering numbers				
Compare and order numbers, using the related vocabulary; use the equals (=) sign	C 3 Finds one more or one less from a group of up to five objects C 7 Finds one more or one less than a number from 1 to 10	• order numbers to 10 • say what number comes next, is one more/less • count back to zero • place 1-10 into ascending order	• can order numbers to 20 • able to recognise which of two numbers is larger or smaller	I can put numbers up to 20 or more in order.
③ Reading and writing numbers				
Read and write numerals from 0 to 20, then beyond; use knowledge of place value to position these numbers on a number track and number line	NLC 5 Recognises numerals 1 to 9 NLC 9 Recognises, counts, orders, writes and uses numbers up to 20	• read, write numbers to 10 • perhaps with some reversal	• can write numbers to 20 correctly • able to recognise where numbers to 20 belong on a number track	I know how to write numbers up to 20. I know where numbers up to 20 or more belong on a number track.

Unit 2 ⬜ Counting, partitioning and calculating

Framework objectives	Assessment focuses		Success criteria for Year 1	Learning outcomes
	Foundation stage profile scale point	Level 1		
④ One more, one less				
Say the number that is 1 more or less than any given number, and 10 more or less for multiples of 10	C 3 Finds one more or one less from a group of up to five objects C 7 Finds one more or one less than a number from 1 to 10	● order numbers to 10 ● say what number comes next, is one more/less	● knows the number that is one more/less than any number to 20 without counting on or back	*I know the number that is one more or one less than any number up to 20 or more.*
⑤ Add a digit				
Relate addition to counting on; recognise that addition can be done in any order; use practical and informal written methods to support the addition of a one-digit number or a multiple of 10 to a one-digit or two-digit number	C 4 Relates addition by combining two groups	● add and subtract numbers of objects to 10 ● begin to add by counting on from the number of objects in the first set	● can count on from the larger number to find a total	*I can add 1, 2, 3, 4, 5, 6, 7, 8 or 9 to numbers up to 20 or more.*
⑥ Under the tub				
Understand subtraction as 'take away' and find a 'difference' by counting up; use practical and informal written methods to support the subtraction of a one-digit number from a one-digit or two-digit number and a multiple of 10 from a two-digit number	C 5 Relates subtraction to taking away	● understand subtraction as 'taking away' objects from a set and finding how many are left	● can find a difference between two numbers by counting up from the smaller number	*I can work out the difference between two numbers.*

Unit 2 ▢ Counting, partitioning and calculating

Framework objectives	Assessment focuses		Success criteria for Year 1	Learning outcomes
	Foundation stage profile scale point	Level 1		
⑦ Dice add ⑧ Dice difference				
Solve problems involving counting, adding, subtracting, doubling or halving in the context of numbers, measures or money, for example to 'pay' and 'give change'	C 8 Uses developing mathematical ideas and methods to solve practical problems	• solve addition/subtraction problems involving up to 10 objects, e.g. ○ given a number work out 'how many more to make...' ○ choose which of given pairs of numbers add to a given total ○ solve measuring problems such as how many balance with... ○ solve problems involving 1p or £1 coins	• able to recognise when a problem requires addition or subtraction to solve it • solves the problem using addition or subtraction	*I can solve a problem or puzzle using adding/ subtracting.*
Describe ways of solving puzzles and problems, explaining choices and decisions orally or using pictures	NLC 8 Uses developing mathematical ideas and methods to solve practical problems	• draw simple conclusions from their work, e.g. with support ○ explain numbers and calculations, how many altogether, how many used or hidden, how many left, how many each, etc	• solves problems by using addition or subtraction, as appropriate • able to talk about how the problem was solved	*I can talk about how I solve problems using adding/ subtracting.*
Use the vocabulary related to addition and subtraction and symbols to describe and record addition and subtraction number sentences	C 6 In practical activities and discussion, begins to use the vocabulary involved in adding and subtracting	• discuss their work, e.g. with support ○ refer to the materials they have used and talk about what they have done, patterns they have noticed, etc • record their work, e.g. ○ record their work with objects, pictures or diagrams ○ begin to use the symbols '+' and '=' to record additions	• can talk about an addition or subtraction • can write an addition or subtraction sentence using +, − and =	*I can talk about adding and subtracting.* *I can use the signs +, − and = when I write addition and subtraction sentences.*

BLOCK A

Activity ①

Prior learning
Children can estimate the number in a group of up to 20 objects. They can check the number by counting.

Framework objective
Count reliably at least 20 objects, recognising that when rearranged the number of objects stays the same; estimate a number of objects that can be checked by counting

Vocabulary
count, guess, how many, estimate, nearly, roughly, close to, about the same as, just over, just under, too many, too few, enough, not enough

Resources
Worksheet: Estimate and count
Classroom resources: tubs, empty margarine pots, empty yogurt pots, items to fill the containers

① Estimate and count

Put items in the pots, limiting the numbers to up to 20. Provide each child with the worksheet 'Estimate and count' and ask them to estimate in pairs how many items are in each container. They should write their estimate on the worksheet before counting the items and recording their count. They can then decide if they made a good estimate. Check that children count each item just once.

Teacher support
Less confident learners: Limit the number of items in containers to up to 10.
More confident learners: Ask these children to fill a different container with up to 20 items. They can then swap containers with a partner and estimate and check how many they have by counting.

Common misconception
Children do not count accurately.
Place items such as cubes on the table. Ask children to count these. Observe their counting strategy. Check that they count each item just once and that they understand that the last item counted gives the total number. Check that children coordinate the 'touch, count and move' procedure.

Probing questions
● How many crayons do you think there are in the tub? Now count them carefully. Are there more or fewer than you thought?
● How could you check the number of crayons?
● How do you know you have counted every crayon just once?

Next steps
Support: Provide further opportunities to estimate and then count a number of items. For example, children can estimate how many pairs of scissors there are in a tub, then count them. See also Year 1 Block A Unit 1.
Extension: Encourage these children to estimate and count beyond 20. See also Year 1 Block A Unit 3.

Activity ②

Prior learning
Children can put numbers up to 20 or more in order.

Framework objective
Compare and order numbers, using the related vocabulary; use the equals (=) sign

Vocabulary
count, compare, order, larger, smaller, largest, smallest

Resources
Resource sheets: Self-assessment, Numeral cards 0-10, Numeral cards 11-20
Classroom resources: paper

② Comparing and ordering numbers

Give each pair of children a set of shuffled 0-20 numeral cards and some paper. The children take it in turns to draw a card and place it on the table so that once all the cards have been drawn they have placed 0 to 20 in order. Ask them to take turns to draw three cards. They decide which is the smallest and which is the largest number. They record the three numbers in order on paper (for example, 8, 12, 17). Decide whether to use the self-assessment sheet for the children to record their achievements and what they need to do next. Ask them to record some of their number trios on the sheet.

Teacher support
Less confident learners: Limit the number range to up to 10 until the children are confident with comparing and ordering these numbers.
More confident learners: Extend the number range to up to 30.

Common misconception
Children do not recognise which is the smaller and larger of two numbers.
Use numeral cards 1-10. Ask children to place these in order on the table in front of them. Slide two of the cards out of line, but so that it is obvious where the cards belong. *Which is the smaller number? Which is the larger number? How do you know that?* Repeat this several times, then shuffle the cards and choose two at random and repeat. Once children are confident with this, extend to three cards.

Probing questions
● Look at these numbers: 8, 3, 12, 20. Which of the numbers is largest? Are any of the numbers larger than 10? Which number is smallest?
● Put the numbers in order, starting with the smallest. How can you check the order?

Next steps
Support: Gradually extend the number range to up to 20, then beyond. Children can do this in pairs, taking turns to draw and order two, then three, cards. See also Year 1 Block A Unit 1.
Extension: Encourage these children to compare and order four or five numbers up to 30. See also Year 1 Block A Unit 3.

BLOCK A

Activity ③

Prior learning
Children know how to write numbers up to 20. They know where numbers up to 20 or more belong on a number track.

Framework objective
Read and write numerals from 0 to 20, then beyond; use knowledge of place value to position these numbers on a number track and number line

Vocabulary
read, write, record

Resources
Interactive activity: Reading and writing numbers
Resource sheet: Self-assessment
Classroom resources: whiteboards and pens

③ Reading and writing numbers

Display the interactive activity 'Reading and writing numbers'. Ask the children to look at the numbers on the screen. They should write down the missing numbers, in number order, on their whiteboards. When you say *Show me*, they hold up their boards. Check who has the answer correct, and who needs more support. Invite children to come to the board to type the correct numbers into the empty spaces to complete each number track. Once they have completed this activity, decide whether to use the self-assessment sheet for the children to record their achievements and what they need to do next.

Teacher support
Less confident learners: Use numbers to 10 until these children are confident with finding the missing numbers.
More confident learners: Extend to numbers to up to 30.

Common misconception
Children do not recognise missing numbers in a series.
Begin with sets of numbers from 1, such as 1, 2, 3, 4, 5. Cover the 4 and 5 and ask children to say what numbers are covered and how they know. Repeat for other sets, gradually extending to up to 20 as confidence grows.

Probing questions
● Look at these numbers: 13, 14, 15, ☐, ☐, 18. Which numbers are covered? As these numbers get bigger, which digits change and which digits stay the same?
● Which numbers do you know that have 1 as the first digit?
● Where are the numbers that start with 'twenty' on the 100-square?

Next steps
Support: Ask the children to count starting from 1. Say 'Stop.' Ask: *What is the next number? And the next?* Repeat this several times. See also Year 1 Block B Unit 1.
Extension: Encourage these children to extend this activity to numbers up to 30 and beyond. See also Year 1 Block A Unit 3.

BLOCK A

Activity ④

Prior learning
Children know the number that is one more or one less than any number up to 20 or more.

Framework objective
Say the number that is 1 more or less than any given number, and 10 more or less for multiples of 10

Vocabulary
one more, one less

Resources
Resource sheets: Self-assessment, Numeral cards 0–10, Numeral cards 11–20

④ One more, one less

Provide each pair of children with numeral cards 1–19, shuffled. The children take turns to take the top card. They say the 'one more' number and the 'one less' number. They can record these in a table with three columns ('One less than', 'My number' and 'One more than'). Check as they work that they are giving the 'one more' and 'one less' numbers quickly and fluently. Decide whether to use the self-assessment sheet for the children to record their achievements and what they need to do next. They can record some of their numbers there, showing which is one more and which is one less.

Teacher support
Less confident learners: Limit the number range to up to 10 to begin with.
More confident learners: Extend the number range to 30.

Common misconception
Children do not know how to find the one more, one less numbers.
Count together from 1 to 10. Repeat this, stopping on 7. *What number is next in the count? So what is one more than 7? What number did we say just before 7? So what number is one less than 7?* Children may find the 'one less' number more difficult to find. If so, practise counting back from 10 down to zero, stopping on, say, 6, and asking: *What number will we say next? So one less than 6 is ___?*

Probing questions
● Use the numbers 15 to 20. Choose a pair of numbers to make this sentence true: □ is one more than □.
● How many different pairs can you find that make the sentence true? Can you make the sentence true with other numbers?

Next steps
Support: Provide further practice in counting forwards and backwards from zero to 10, then extend this to 20 and beyond. Stop the count. *What is one more than the number we just said? What is one less than the number we just said?* See also Year 1 Block B Unit 1.
Extension: Encourage these children to extend their counting well beyond 20, to 30, then 40. Repeat the activity for the one more, one less numbers for up to 30, then 40. See also Year 1 Block B Unit 2.

Activity ⑤

Prior learning
Children can add 1, 2, 3, 4, 5, 6, 7, 8 or 9 to numbers up to 20 or more.

Framework objective
Relate addition to counting on; recognise that addition can be done in any order; use practical and informal written methods to support the addition of a one-digit number or a multiple of 10 to a one-digit or two-digit number

Vocabulary
add, plus, makes, sum, total, altogether

Resources
Resource sheets: Self-assessment, Numeral cards 0-10, Numeral cards 11-20, Number lines 0-30

⑤ Add a digit

Ask the children to work in pairs. They will need a shuffled stack of numeral cards 1-20 and a separate stack of numeral cards 1-9. They take turns to take the top card from each stack. They write an addition sentence and find the answer by counting on mentally. They return their cards to the bottom of the correct stack. Decide whether to use the self-assessment sheet for the children to record their achievements and what they need to do next.

Teacher support
Less confident learners: Limit the number range to 1-9 and 1-9. Encourage the children to count on mentally once they have found the answer using a number line.
More confident learners: Ask these children to try to answer all their addition questions using mental counting on.

Common misconception
Children cannot count on mentally to find addition totals.
Use small numbers, up to 6. *What is 4 add 3?* Show children how to count on, keeping a tally with their fingers. Say together: *4 add 3 is 4 add 5, 6, 7. So 4 add 3 is 7.* Repeat this for other additions until children are confident with this method.

Probing questions
● What is 19 add 5? What can you use to help you find the answer?
● Someone said: *19 plus 5 makes 23*. Can you show how you know that this is not the right answer?

Next steps
Support: Provide further opportunities for adding by counting on. This could be part of an oral and mental starter. Keep the numbers small to begin in. See also Year 1 Block A Unit 1.
Extension: Provide opportunities for the children to add a one-digit to a two-digit number, extending the two-digit numbers beyond 20. Ask them to explain how they found the answer working mentally. See also Year 1 Block D Unit 2.

Activity ⑥

Prior learning	**Framework objective**
Children can work out the difference between two numbers.	Understand subtraction as 'take away' and find a 'difference' by counting up; use practical and informal written methods to support the subtraction of a one-digit number from a one-digit or two-digit number and a multiple of 10 from a two-digit number

Vocabulary
subtract, minus, take away, leaves, difference

Resources
Resource sheets: Self-assessment, Number lines 0–20
Classroom resources: counting items (such as cubes), empty margarine tub

⑥ Under the tub

Provide each child with the resource sheet 'Number lines 0–20'. Together, count out eight cubes. Place some of the cubes under the margarine tub. Show the children what is left. *How many cubes are under the tub?* Ask them to use a number line to find the answer and write an appropriate subtraction sentence. Repeat this for different starting amounts. Include 'difference'. *There are 14 cubes here. I have put some under the tub. There are 9 left. What is the difference between 14 and 9? So how many are under the tub?* Decide whether to use the self-assessment sheet for the children to record their achievements and what they need to do next.

Teacher support
Less confident learners: Limit the number of cubes to 10 or less.
More confident learners: Ask these children to work mentally, finding the difference by counting up from the smaller to the larger number.

Common misconception
Children do not understand 'difference'.
Put out a tower of five cubes and a tower of three cubes. *Which has more? How many more? Which has fewer? How many fewer? So what is the difference between the two towers?* Repeat this for other quantities of cubes. Provide number lines for children to mark the numbers on. Ask them to count up from the smaller to the larger number.

Probing questions
● What is 15 take away 6? How did you work that out? How could you check it?
● Make up another 'take away'/subtraction question with answer 9.
● What is the difference between 5 and 12? Show that using counters/on a number line/on paper.

Next steps
Support: Gradually extend the size of the numbers to up to 20, but keep the difference small (say up to 5). See also Year 1 Block A Unit 1.
Extension: Extend the number range to up to 30. Encourage the children to work mentally, by counting up, in order to find the difference. See also Year 1 Block D Unit 2.

BLOCK A

Activities ⑦ and ⑧

Prior learning
Children can solve a problem or puzzle using adding/subtracting. They can talk about how they solve problems using adding/subtracting. They can talk about adding and subtracting, and can use the signs +, - and = when they write addition and subtraction sentences.

Framework objectives
● Solve problems involving counting, adding, subtracting, doubling or halving in the context of numbers, measures or money, for example to 'pay' and 'give change'
● Describe ways of solving puzzles and problems, explaining choices and decisions orally or using pictures
● **Use the vocabulary related to addition and subtraction and symbols to describe and record addition and subtraction number sentences**

Vocabulary
pattern, answer, number sentence, sign, operation, explain, show me, read, write, record, count, compare, order, the same number as, as many as, equal to, equals, sign, more, most, less, least, greater, greatest, larger, largest, bigger, biggest, fewer, fewest, smaller, smallest, before, after, halfway, add, plus, makes, sum, total, altogether, subtract, minus, take away, leaves, difference, how many?, how many more to make?, how many more is ... than ...?, how much more is ...?, how many fewer is ... than ...?, how much less is ...?, what is the difference between ...?

Resources
Resource sheets: Number lines 0–20, Self-assessment
Classroom resources: 1–6 dice, paper

⑦ Dice add

Give each pair of children two 1–6 dice and some paper. Explain that they have ten minutes to find all the addition facts that they can from tossing the two dice. They should record their results on paper as addition sentences. Observe how children tackle the problem and their recording. Decide whether to use the self-assessment sheet for the children to record their achievements and what they need to do next. They can record some of their number sentences to demonstrate that they can solve a problem and record appropriately.

Teacher support
Less confident learners: Work together as a group to solve the problem.
More confident learners: Ask these children to find a way to order their results, and to check that they have not duplicated any number sentences.

Common misconception
Children do not have mental strategies for adding.
Ask: *What is 3 add 2? Say 3 add 4, 5. So 3 add 2 is 5.* At this stage children can keep a tally with their fingers as they count on. Repeat for other additions until children can calculate simple addition mentally.

Probing questions
● I think of a number and add 2. My answer is 14. What was my number? How do you know you need to add/subtract?
● How did you solve the problem? How did the apparatus/your recording help you?

Next steps
Support: Encourage these children to use mental methods for addition of small numbers. Include addition in oral and mental starters so that they begin to develop rapid recall of facts. See also Year 1 Block E Unit 1.
Extension: Encourage the children to extend their ability to recall addition facts for addition of numbers to 10. Include addition in oral and mental starters so that they begin to develop rapid recall of facts. See also Year 1 Block E Unit 2.

⑧ Dice difference

Give each pair of children two 1-6 dice and some paper. Explain that they have ten minutes to find all the difference facts that they can from tossing the two dice. They should record their results on paper as subtraction sentences. Observe how they tackle the problem and their recording. Decide whether to use the self-assessment sheet for the children to record their achievements and what they need to do next. They can record some of their number sentences to demonstrate that they can solve a problem and record appropriately.

Teacher support
Less confident learners: Work together as a group to solve the problem.
More confident learners: Ask these children to find a way to order their results, and to check that they have not duplicated any number sentences.

Common misconception
Children do not have strategies for finding the difference between two numbers.
Provide the resource sheet 'Number lines 0-20'. Ask children to use the number line to find the difference between 5 and 2. Ask them to mark 2 and 5 and to join them with a loop above the numbers. Now ask them to count up from 2 to 5, keeping a tally with their fingers. Repeat this for other small numbers until they have a strategy for finding the difference.

Probing questions
● Choose two number cards (0-9) and make up some additions and subtractions using those numbers. Try to put them in different ways. For example, $3 + 5 = 8$, 3 and 5 more is 8, 5 take away 3 leaves 2, $5 - 3 = 2$, 5 is 2 more than 3, the difference between 5 and 3 is 2.

Next steps
Support: Encourage these children to use number lines or mental methods for finding the difference of small numbers. Include this in oral and mental starters so that they begin to develop rapid recall of facts. See also Year 1 Block E Unit 1.
Extension: Encourage these children to extend their ability to recall subtraction facts for numbers to 10, and for finding the difference between two small numbers. Include these in oral and mental starters so they begin to develop rapid recall of facts. See also Year 1 Block E Unit 2.

Unit 3 ▨ Counting, partitioning and calculating

Introduction

In this unit children develop their ability to explain how they solved problems, and the decisions they made, speaking in an audible voice. They continue to compare and order numbers, and extend their counting skills by counting on or back in ones from a two-digit number as part of a lesson starter. They read, write and order numerals from 0 to 20, then extend this, using a 100-square as an aid. They say the number that is one or ten more or less than a given number, extending this to beyond 30. They continue to develop their skills in addition and subtraction, and recognise that if an addition fact is known they can find the corresponding subtraction fact. They can use a given fact such as 6 + 2 to find 16 + 2 and if they know, for example, 9 − 3, they can find 19 − 3. They use their acquired knowledge to solve problems.

Framework objectives	Assessment focuses		Success criteria for Year 1	Learning outcomes
	Foundation stage profile scale point	Level 1		
① Number order				
Compare and order numbers, using the related vocabulary; use the equals (=) sign	C 3 Finds one more or one less from a group of up to five objects C 7 Finds one more or one less than a number from 1 to 10	● order numbers to 10 ● say what number comes next, is one more/less ● count back to zero ● place 1-10 into ascending order	● can say the counting numbers in order to up to 20 and beyond ● recognises which numbers will fit between two other numbers up to 20 and beyond	I know the order of numbers up to 20 and more.
② Bundles of ten				
Read and write numerals from 0 to 20, then beyond; use knowledge of place value to position these numbers on a number track and number line	NLC 5 Recognises numerals 1 to 9 NLC 9 Recognises, counts, orders, writes and uses numbers up to 20	● read, write numbers to 10 ● perhaps with some reversal	● can write numbers to 20 and beyond correctly ● can find given numbers on a number line/100-square	I can write numbers up to 20 and more. I can find them on a number line/100-square.

Unit 3 📖 Counting, partitioning and calculating

Framework objectives	Assessment focuses		Success criteria for Year 1	Learning outcomes
	Foundation stage profile scale point	Level 1		
③ Ten more, ten less				
Say the number that is 1 more or less than any given number, and 10 more or less for multiples of 10	C 3 Finds one more or one less from a group of up to five objects C 7 Finds one more or one less than a number from 1 to 10	• order numbers to 10 • say what number comes next, is one more/less	• knows the number that is ten more/less than any number to 100 without counting on or back	*I can say the number that is ten more or ten less than 10, 20, 30...*
④ Adding tens				
Relate addition to counting on; recognise that addition can be done in any order; use practical and informal written methods to support the addition of a one-digit number or a multiple of 10 to a one-digit or two-digit number	C 4 Relates addition by combining two groups	• order numbers to 10 • say what number comes next, is one more/less • understand addition as finding the total of two or more sets of objects	• can add 10, 20, 30... to any number up to 50 by counting on in tens	*I can add 10, 20, 30... to any number up to 50.*
⑤ Add or subtract 20				
Understand subtraction as 'take away' and find a 'difference' by counting up; use practical and informal written methods to support the subtraction of a one-digit number from a one-digit or two-digit number and a multiple of 10 from a two-digit number	C 5 Relates subtraction to taking away	• understand subtraction as 'taking away' objects from a set and finding how many are left	• can add or subtract 20 to any number by counting on or back	*I can add or subtract 20 to a number and tell you the answer.*

Unit 3 ⬜ Counting, partitioning and calculating

Framework objectives	Assessment focuses		Success criteria for Year 1	Learning outcomes
	Foundation stage profile scale point	Level 1		
⑥ Addition challenge ⑦ Subtraction challenge				
Describe ways of solving puzzles and problems, explaining choices and decisions orally or using pictures	NLC 8 Uses developing mathematical ideas and methods to solve practical problems	• discuss their work, e.g. with support • respond to questions and ideas from peers and adults • refer to the materials they have used and talk about what they have done, patterns they have noticed, etc	• able to describe a problem • able to describe the steps taken to solve the problem	*I can explain how I solve problems.*
Use the vocabulary related to addition and subtraction and symbols to describe and record addition and subtraction number sentence	C 6 In practical activities and discussion, begins to use the vocabulary involved in adding and subtracting	• record their work, e.g. • record their work with objects, pictures or diagrams • begin to use the symbols '+' and '=' to record additions	• recognises 'take away' and 'difference' and can use these terms to describe a subtraction question • can write an addition or subtraction sentence using +, - and =	*I can ask addition and subtraction questions in different ways. I can use the signs +, − and = when I write addition and subtraction sentences.*
⑧ Double or halve				
Solve problems involving counting, adding, subtracting, doubling or halving in the context of numbers, measures or money, for example to 'pay' and 'give change'	C 8 Uses developing mathematical ideas and methods to solve practical problems	• solve addition/subtraction problems involving up to 10 objects	• recognises when a problem requires doubling or halving to solve it • solves the problem using doubling or halving	*I can solve a problem or puzzle by using doubling and halving.*

Activity ①

Prior learning
Children know the order of numbers up to 20 and more.

Framework objective
Compare and order numbers, using the related vocabulary; use the equals (=) sign

Vocabulary list
count, compare, order

Resources
Resource sheets: Blank number lines, Numeral cards 0-20, Self-assessment

① Number order

Give each pair of children a shuffled set of 0-20 numeral cards. They take turns to take the top two cards and write these numbers on the resource sheet 'Blank number lines'. They should then write another number which is between the two drawn numbers. Their partner checks that they agree. If it is not possible to place a whole number between the drawn numbers (for example, 16 and 17), then they explain to their partner why it is not possible. Observe how children make their decisions about placing numbers and how they choose their in-between numbers. Decide whether to use the self-assessment sheet for the children to record their achievements and what they need to do next.

Teacher support
Less confident learners: Limit this at first to numbers to 10.
More confident learners: Challenge these children to write two whole numbers between their drawn numbers. If they cannot do this, they should be ready to explain why it is not possible.

Common misconception
Children cannot order numbers to 20.
Begin with numbers to 10. Use a shuffled set of cards and challenge children to place these in order. Extend to 20. Place two cards on the table. Ask children to read the numbers and place them in number order. For example, for 17 and 6 they would place them from the left: 6, 17. Ask children to find a number from the cards left to fit between 6 and 17. Repeat, each time ensuring that all the cards on the table are in order. Continue until all cards have been placed in order.

Probing questions
● Give me a number between 15 and 21. Is it closer to 15 or 21? Show me why on a blank number line.
● What number is halfway between 15 and 21? How did you work it out?

Next steps
Support: Extend the range of numbers that the children can compare and order up to 20 over time. Ask the children to work in pairs to order a stack of 0-20 cards. They begin by placing any two cards on the table, and then add the others, one at a time, in number order. See also Year 1 Block A Unit 2.
Extension: Encourage these children to extend their number experience by comparing numbers to 30, then 40, and then any number to 100. See also Year 2 Block A Unit 1.

BLOCK A

Activity ②

Prior learning
Children can write numbers up to 20 and more, and can find them on a number line/100-square.

Framework objective
Read and write numerals from 0 to 20, then beyond; use knowledge of place value to position these numbers on a number track and number line

Vocabulary
one, two, three, hundred; first, second, third; ones, tens, 'teens' number, exchange, digit

Resources
Resource sheets: 100-square, Self-assessment
Classroom resources: elastic bands, straws

② Bundles of ten

Write some two-digit numbers on the board: 12, 19, 31, 42 and so on. Ask the children to work in pairs and to make each number as a tens and units number, using the straws and elastic bands. Then ask them to find the number on the resource sheet '100-square' and circle it. They record each number in tens and units like this: 12 is the same as 1 ten and 2 units. Decide whether to use the self-assessment sheet for the children to record their achievements and what they need to do next. They can record their numbers there.

Teacher support
Less confident learners: Limit the range of numbers to up to 20 to begin with.
More confident learners: Provide more two-digit numbers beyond 50.

Common misconception
Children do not recognise that numbers with two digits are made from tens and units.
Ask children to count out, say, 11 straws. Ask them to bundle the straws into a ten and ones. *How many tens do you have? How many ones? So 11 is the same as 1 ten and 1 unit.* Write this as a sentence. Continue with other numbers up to 20 until children realise the significance of each digit in a two-digit number.

Probing questions
● Put these numbers in order, starting with the smallest: 15, 19, 12. What did you look for when you ordered them?
● Use these ten straws and single straws. Pick up 12 straws. How do you know you have 12?
● How do you tell the difference between 12 and 21?

Next steps
Support: Provide further experience of bundling straws to make tens and units numbers. Extend this to asking questions such as: *Here is the number 19. How many tens are there? How many units? What about the number 23?* See also Year 1 Block A Unit 2.
Extension: When the children are confident with the place value of numbers to 100, extend this to three-digit numbers. See also Year 2 Block A Unit 1.

Activity ③

Prior learning
Children can say the number that is 10 more or 10 less than 10, 20, 30...

Framework objective
Say the number that is 1 more or less than any given number, and 10 more or less for multiples of 10

Vocabulary
ten more, ten less

Resources
Worksheet: Ten more, ten less
Resource sheet: 100-square
Classroom resources: 10-pence coins

③ Ten more, ten less

Hand out the worksheet 'Ten more, ten less'. Ask the children to write in the numbers that are 10 more and 10 less than the numbers that are given. They then use their own numbers to complete the sentences. As they work, discuss with them how they made their choices. Provide the resource sheet '100-square' and ask the children to show how they know that their number sentences are true.

Teacher support
Less confident learners: Concentrate on 'one more' and 'one less.'
More confident learners: Challenge these children to choose some numbers that are more than 100.

Common misconception
Children cannot say the ten more or ten less numbers.
Starting from zero, count in tens. Stop on 70. Ask: *What is the last number that we said? What is the next number in the count? So 10 more than 70 is 80. What is the number before 70? So 10 less than 70 is 60.* Repeat this for other tens.

Probing questions
● Using two of these numbers (10, 20, 30), make this sentence true: □ is 10 more than □. How do you know you are correct?
● Pick up some 10-pence coins. How much have you got altogether? Put 10p back. How much do you have now? How did you work that out?

Next steps
Support: Include counting in tens as part of an oral and mental starter. Stop on, say, 50 and ask: *What is 10 more than 50? What is 10 less than 50? How do you know?* See also Year 1 Block A Unit 2.
Extension: Encourage these children to find 10 more or less than any two-digit number. See also Year 2 Block A Unit 1.

Activity ④

Prior learning
Children can add 10, 20, 30... to any number up to 50.

Framework objective
Relate addition to counting on; recognise that addition can be done in any order; use practical and informal written methods to support the addition of a one-digit number or a multiple of 10 to a one-digit or two-digit number

Vocabulary
add, plus, makes, sum, total, altogether, pattern, answer, number sentence, sign, operation

Resources
Resource sheets: Blank number lines, 100-square (folded so that only 1–50 are visible), Self-assessment
Classroom resources: counters, paper, dice marked 10, 10, 20, 30, 40, 50

④ Adding tens

In pairs, the children take turns to toss a counter onto the folded 100-square and throw the dice. They add their number from the 100-square to the dice number and record this as an addition sentence. They can use the resource sheet 'Blank number lines' to count on, or they can open out the 100-square. Decide whether to use the self-assessment sheet for the children to record their achievements and what they need to do next. They can record some of their addition sentences on the sheet.

Teacher support
Less confident learners: Limit to adding 10 to numbers to 30.
More confident learners: Extend the activity to adding tens to any number on the 100-square.

Common misconception
Children do not have a reliable strategy for adding tens to any number to 50.
Use a 100-square and numbers to 20. Ask children to add 10 to 15. They can count on the 100-square to do this. *What do you notice about your answer?* Discuss how the tens digit has increased by 1 and the units digit has stayed the same. Repeat this for other examples. Extend to adding 20, then 30.

Probing questions
● 5 + 6 + 2 = 13, 5 + 2 + 6 = □. Will the second answer be smaller, the same as or bigger than the first answer? How do you know?
● Make up a problem about adding 10 or 20 to ask me. How will you know if I get the right answer?

Next steps
Support: Extend from adding 10, to adding 20, 30, and so on. Over time, increase the size of the two-digit numbers to up to 50. See also Year 1 Block A Unit 2.
Extension: Challenge these children to add any two-digit decade number to any number on a 100-square. Invite them to explain how they worked out the answer, and any number patterns that they used. See also Year 2 Block A Unit 1.

Activity ⑤

Prior learning
Children can add or subtract 20 to a number and tell you the answer.

Framework objective
Understand subtraction as 'take away' and find a 'difference' by counting up; use practical and informal written methods to support the subtraction of a one-digit number from a one-digit or two-digit number and a multiple of 10 from a two-digit number

Vocabulary
subtract, minus, take away, leaves, difference

Resources
Resource sheets: Blank number lines, 100-square (folded so that only 31–50 are visible), Self-assessment
Classroom resources: counters, paper

⑤ Add or subtract 20

Ask the children to work in pairs. One child will be 'Add 20', and the other will be 'Subtract 20'. Explain that they will take turns to toss the counter onto the folded 100-square and add 20 to or subtract 20 from the number they get. They should record this as an addition or subtraction sentence. They may use the resource sheet 'Blank number lines' to help them to find the answer, count on or back on the 100-square, or use mental patterns to help them to find the answer. Decide whether to use the self-assessment sheet for the children to record their achievements and what they need to do next.

Teacher support
Less confident learners: Limit to adding or subtracting 10, with numbers to 20.
More confident learners: Use the numbers 21 to 100 with this group.

Common misconception
Children do not have a reliable strategy for adding 20 to any number up to 50, or for subtracting 20 from any number from 21 to 50.
Use a 100-square and numbers to 20. Ask children to add 20 to 15. They can count on a 100-square to do this. *What do you notice about your answer?* Discuss how the tens digit has increased by 2 and the units digit has stayed the same. Repeat for other examples. Repeat for subtracting 20 from numbers between 31 and 40. Discuss what happens to the digits.

Probing questions
● What is 37 take away 10? How did you work that out? Can you show me how using cubes/a number line/a 100-square? What is 37 take away 20?
● Make up some difference questions with the answer 5. How do you solve them using counters/a number line?

Next steps
Support: Over time, extend to adding or subtracting 20 from numbers to 30, 40 then 50. See also Year 1 Block A Unit 2.
Extension: Challenge these children to subtract 30, 40, 50 from numbers 50 to 100. See also Year 2 Block A Unit 1.

BLOCK A

Activities ⑥ and ⑦

Prior learning
Children can explain how they solve problems. They can ask addition and subtraction questions in different ways. They can use the signs +, − and = when they write addition and subtraction sentences.

Framework objectives
● Describe ways of solving puzzles and problems, explaining choices and decisions orally or using pictures
● **Use the vocabulary related to addition and subtraction and symbols to describe and record addition and subtraction number sentences**

Vocabulary
pattern, answer, number sentence, sign, operation, explain, show me, read, write, record, count, compare, order, add, plus, makes, sum, total, altogether, subtract, minus, take away, leaves, difference, how many?, how many more to make ...?, how many more is ... than ...?, how much more is ...?, how many fewer is ... than ...?, how much less is ...?, what is the difference between ...?

Resources
Display pages: Addition challenge, Subtraction challenge
Resource sheets: Blank number lines, Self-assessment
Classroom resources: interlocking cubes

⑥ Addition challenge

Ask the children to work individually. Show the display page 'Addition challenge'. Invite the children to calculate the answer to the first number sentence. Then read the next two sentences together and ask what the answers are. Click on the 'show' button to reveal the answers. Now invite the children to find five different number sentences that total 17. They should write each number sentence in three different ways. They can use the resource sheet 'Blank number lines' to help them if necessary. Ask them to explain how they solved the problem. Decide whether to use the self-assessment sheet for the children to record their achievements and what they need to do next.

Teacher support
Less confident learners: Do this as a group activity and reduce the total to up to 10.
More confident learners: Challenge these children to write ten different number sentences with the answer of 17.

Common misconception
Children do not have a strategy for addition where the answer is a teen number.
Provide an empty number line and say: *What is 11 add 2? Write the number 11 on your number line. Now count on 2. What number do you reach? Write in 13. So 11 add 2 is 13.* Now ask children to do this mentally. They can keep track of how many they count on their fingers: *11 and 12, 13.* Repeat for other additions until children have a strategy with which they feel confident.

Probing questions
● How did you solve the problem? How did the apparatus/your recording help you? How did you check that your solution works?
● Make up some additions with the answer 15. Put them in different ways (for example, 10 + 5 = 15, the total of 10 and 5 is 15, 10 and 5 more makes 15).

Next steps
Support: Provide oral and mental starters that include addition to 10. Over time, extend the range for addition. See also Year 1 Block A Unit 2.
Extension: Encourage these children to complete additions using mental methods. See also Year 1 Block B Unit 3.

⑦ Subtraction challenge

Ask the children to work individually. Show the display page 'Subtraction challenge'. Ask the children to calculate the answer to the first number sentence. Then read the next sentence together and ask what the answer is. Click on the 'show' button to reveal the answers. Now invite the children to find five different subtraction sentences that have the answer 4. Ask them to write each in three different ways. They can use the resource sheet 'Blank number lines' to help them if necessary. Ask them to explain how they solved the problem. Decide whether to use the self-assessment sheet for children to record their achievements and what they need to do next.

Teacher support

Less confident learners: Do this as a group activity. Check that the children understand subtraction as both 'take away' and as 'difference'.
More confident learners: Challenge these children to write ten different number sentences with the answer of 4.

Common misconception

Children do not have a strategy for subtraction as 'take away' or as 'difference'. Use some interlocking cubes. Make a tower of 7. *How many will be left if I take away 3?* Invite children to suggest ways of finding the answer. Repeat this for other 'take away' questions. For difference, make two towers, one of seven and one of four interlocking cubes. Place the towers together. *What is the difference between 7 and 4?* Check that children count on from 4 to 7. They can keep a tally with their fingers as they count up.

Probing questions

● How did you solve the problem? How did the apparatus/your recording help you? How did you check that your solution works?
● Make up some subtractions with the answer 5. Try to put them in different ways (for example, 11 − 6 = 5, the difference between 6 and 11 is 5).

Next steps

Support: Provide oral and mental starters that include 'take away' and 'difference' questions. See also Year 1 Block A Unit 2.
Extension: Encourage these children to complete subtraction using mental methods. See also Year 1 Block B Unit 3.

Activity ⑧

Prior learning
Children can solve a problem or puzzle by using doubling and halving.

Framework objective
Solve problems involving counting, adding, subtracting, doubling or halving in the context of numbers, measures or money, for example to 'pay' and 'give change'

Vocabulary
pattern, answer, number sentence, sign, operation, explain, show me, read, write, record, double, half, halve

Resources
Interactive activity: Double or halve
Worksheet: Double or halve
Resource sheet: Blank number lines
Classroom resources: interlocking cubes, whiteboards and pens

⑧ Double or halve

Begin with an oral and mental starter. Reveal the interactive activity 'Double or halve'. Rather than playing bingo, ask the children to write the answers on their whiteboards. When you say *Show me*, they should hold up their boards for you to check. Now provide the worksheet 'Double or halve'. There are four word problems to be solved. The children may prefer to read the problems together before they begin.

Teacher support
Less confident learners: Work as a group to solve the problems.
More confident learners: Challenge these children to write their own double or halve problem for the others to solve.

Common misconception
Children do not have strategies for doubling or halving.
Begin by counting in 2s from zero to 20 and back again. Give children the resource sheet 'Blank number lines'. Make two towers of four cubes each. *How many cubes are there altogether? How did you work that out?* If children are unsure, show them how to count on from 4 on the number line. Repeat.
Ask children to halve 8. They can use the cubes to make a tower of 8 and snap it into two equal parts. Model this on the number line, too. Repeat for other even numbers.

Probing questions
● Apples cost 6 pence each. How much do two apples cost altogether? How do you know that you need to double the number?
● Could you use beads/coins to show how you know you are right?
● Can you make up a problem where you would use 'double 10 = 20' to solve it?

Next steps
Support: Provide further opportunities to practise recall of double and half facts. See also Year 1 Block D Unit 2.
Extension: Encourage these children to write their own double or halve problems for their partners to solve. See also Year 1 Block D Unit 3.

These activities can be used at the end of this block to assess those children that you think have achieved the objectives.

Hundred square

Objective
Read and write numerals from 0 to 20, then beyond; use knowledge of place value to position these numbers on a number track and number line

Assessment focus
Level 1: Read, write numbers to 10, perhaps with some reversal
Foundation stage profile scale points: Recognises numerals 1 to 9. Recognises, counts, orders, writes and uses numbers up to 20

Learning outcomes
● I know how to write numbers up to 20.
● I can read numbers on a number track.
● I know where numbers up to 20 or more belong on a number track.
● I can write numbers up to 20 and more.
● I can find them on a number line/100-square.

There are three parts to this activity, which can be set all at once or over the course of a week.

1. Display the interactive activity '100-square'. Say a number and invite the children to describe its position on the square. *Where is number 5? 15? 25? Where is 19? 17? 30?* Observe who is answering confidently, and who is unsure about this.
2. Provide whiteboards and pens. Explain that you will give a description of a number and that the children should write the number on their whiteboards. When you say *Show me* they should hold up their boards for you to see. Check who has the correct answer, and who needs more practice of this. Say, for example: *My number is one more than 5... 1 less than 8... double 5... half of 20...* and so on.
3. Provide the resource sheet 'Number track 0–20'. Say a number and ask the children to highlight it on the number track. *Highlight number 4... 10... 12. Highlight the number that is 1 more than 16... 1 less than 18.* Decide whether to use the self-assessment sheet and attach to the resource sheet as evidence of what they can do.

Adding and subtracting

Objective
Use the vocabulary related to addition and subtraction and symbols to describe and record addition and subtraction number sentences

Assessment focus
Level 1: Record their work, e.g. with objects, pictures or diagrams; begin to use the symbols '+' and '=' to record additions
Foundation stage profile scale points: Begins to use the vocabulary involved in adding and subtracting

Learning outcomes
● I can talk about adding/subtracting.
● I can record additions/subtractions.
● I can ask addition and subtraction questions in different ways.
● I can use the signs +, – and = when I write addition and subtraction sentences.

Ask the children to work in pairs. They will need a set of 1–10 numeral cards and the worksheet 'Adding and subtracting'. The children take turns to draw two cards from the shuffled stack. They add and subtract the two numbers and write addition and subtraction sentences. Ask them to write the sentences in different ways (for example, 4 + 5 = 9, 4 and 5 more is 9, 5 – 4 = 1, the difference between 4 and 5 is 1). Encourage the children to discuss how they can record each number sentence.

Units 1, 2 & 3 ◾ Periodic assessment

Number sentences

Objective
Describe ways of solving puzzles and problems, explaining choices and decisions orally or using pictures

Assessment focus
Level 1: Discuss their work, e.g. with support respond to questions and ideas from peers and adults; refer to the materials they have used and talk about what they have done, patterns they have noticed, etc

Foundation stage profile scale points: Uses developing mathematical ideas and methods to solve practical problems

Learning outcome
● I can explain how I solve problems.

Explain to the children that they will be solving problems and explaining how they did this. Say: *The answer is 5. How many different number sentences can you make with the answer of 5? Remember: you can write addition and subtraction sentences.* Give the children a few minutes to write their number sentences. Ask: *How did you set about this task? Did you count in your heads? Who just knew some number sentences with the answer of 5? What apparatus did you use?* Observe the confidence of the children in explaining how they solved the problem. Once they have completed this activity, decide whether to use the self-assessment sheet for the children to record their achievements and what they need to do next.

Number track 0–20

0	1	2	3	4	5	6	7	8	9	10	11	12	13	14	15	16	17	18	19	20

BLOCK A

Name _____ Date _____

Adding and subtracting

Work with a partner. Use a set of 1–10 numeral cards.

◀ Take turns to draw two cards.

◀ Write an addition sentence using your card numbers.
Then write it in a different way.

Card numbers: _____

Addition sentence: _____

Addition sentence: _____

◀ Write a subtraction sentence using your card numbers.
Then write it in a different way.

Card numbers: _____

Subtraction sentence: _____

Subtraction sentence: _____

◀ Repeat this activity again.

Card numbers: _____

Addition sentence: _____

Addition sentence: _____

Card numbers: _____

Subtraction sentence: _____

Subtraction sentence: _____

How easy?

Red
Amber
Green

How do you think you have done?

_____

_____

BLOCK B
Securing number facts, understanding shape

Expected prior learning
Check that children can already:
- make and talk about simple patterns using numbers and shapes
- say and use the number names in order in familiar contexts and recognise numerals 1 to 9
- count reliably up to ten objects
- use language such as 'more' or 'less' to compare two numbers
- find one more or one less than a number from 1 to 10, using resources
- select two groups of objects to make a given total
- use language such as 'circle' or 'bigger' to describe the shape and size of solids and flat shapes
- sort objects into groups and explain how they sorted them.

Objectives overview
The text in this diagram identifies the focus of mathematics learning within the block.

Key aspects of learning
- Problem solving
- Information processing
- Evaluation
- Communication

Patterns and properties of numbers and shapes

Reading and writing numerals from 0 to 20, then beyond

Ordering numbers on a number line

Estimating and counting at least 20 objects

Recognising that when rearranged the quantity stays the same

BLOCK B: Securing number facts, understanding shape

Early addition and subtraction using related language and symbols including equals (=)

Solving problems and puzzles involving understanding of numbers and operations; explaining their methods and justifying their decisions

Deriving and recalling pairs of numbers that total 10

Beginning to work out and recall addition facts for totals to at least 10 with corresponding subtraction facts

Unit 1 ◻ Securing number facts, understanding shape

Introduction

In this unit children are encouraged to find and explain patterns and relationships. By this stage they are expected to listen and concentrate and to sustain this for the whole of the main activity. In order to encourage children to use what they are learning, incorporate counting, addition and subtraction into home-area and mini-world activities. It would be useful to have a class shop where children can act out the roles of both shopkeeper and customer. Provide some writing materials so that children can make lists and write numbers in context.

BLOCK B

Framework objectives	Assessment focuses		Success criteria for Year 1	Learning outcomes
	Foundation stage profile scale point	Level 1		
① Domino pattern ⑧ Sorting shapes ⑨ Pictures, models and patterns				
Describe simple patterns and relationships involving numbers or shapes; decide whether examples satisfy given conditions	SSM 4 Talks about, recognises and recreates simple patterns	● recognise and use a simple pattern or relationship, e.g. with support ● copy and continue a simple pattern of objects, shapes or numbers	● can copy a simple pattern using numbers or shapes ● recognises when a pattern has a missing piece and can place the piece appropriately ● can continue a simple pattern	*I can use numbers or shapes to copy and continue a simple pattern.*
② How many items?				
Count reliably at least 20 objects, recognising that when rearranged the number of objects stays the same; estimate a number of objects that can be checked by counting	NLC 6 Counts reliably up to 10 everyday objects	● count up to 10 objects, e.g. ● estimate and check a number	● can count accurately to at least 20 ● uses proficiently a counting strategy such as coordinating touch/ point, move item and say the number name ● knows that the last number said represents how many in the set	*I can count at least 20 objects and know that the last number I say is how many there are altogether.*
③ Numerals				
Read and write numerals from 0 to 20, then beyond; use knowledge of place value to position these numbers on a number track and number line	NLC 5 Recognises numerals 1 to 9 NLC 9 Recognises, counts, orders, writes and uses numbers up to 20	● count up to 10 objects, e.g. ● estimate and check a number ● read, write numbers to 10 ● perhaps with some reversal ● order numbers to 10 ● say what number comes next, is one more/less ● count back to zero ● place 1–10 into ascending order ● point to first, second, etc in a line	● can read numbers up to 20 ● can write numbers to 20 accurately ● can order numbers to 20 on a number track or number line ● uses knowledge of place value to recognise the position of a number in an order	*I can read, write and order numbers up to 20.*

Unit 1 ▣ Securing number facts, understanding shape

Framework objectives	Assessment focuses		Success criteria for Year 1	Learning outcomes
	Foundation stage profile scale point	Level 1		

④ Number line: 1 more, 1 less ⑤ Ten more, ten less questions

Framework objectives	Foundation stage profile scale point	Level 1	Success criteria for Year 1	Learning outcomes
Say the number that is 1 more or less than any given number, and 10 more or less for multiples of 10	C 3 Finds one more or one less from a group of up to five objects C 7 Finds one more or one less than a number from 1 to 10	● order numbers to 10 ● say what number comes next, is one more/less	● can use a number line, 100-square or apparatus to find the number that is 1 more/less than a given number ● can find the number that is 10 more/less than a given decade number	*I can use counters or the number line/100-square to find the number that is one more or one less than a number.* *I can find the number that is ten more or ten less for a particular tens number.*

⑥ Adding to 5 ⑦ Make a ten

Framework objectives	Foundation stage profile scale point	Level 1	Success criteria for Year 1	Learning outcomes
Solve problems involving counting, adding, subtracting, doubling or halving in the context of numbers, measures or money, for example to 'pay' and 'give change'	C 8 Uses developing mathematical ideas and methods to solve practical problems	● use mathematics as an integral part of classroom activities, e.g. with support ● engage with practical mathematical activities involving sorting, counting and measuring by direct comparison ● begin to understand the relevance of mathematical ideas to everyday situations by using them in role-play	● recognises key words in a problem or puzzle ● knows what the key words mean ● can identify the mathematics required to solve the problem or puzzle from the key words	*I can begin to solve a problem or puzzle by deciding what the important information is.*
Derive and recall all pairs of numbers with a total of 10 and addition facts for totals to at least 5; work out the corresponding subtraction facts	C 4 Relates addition by combining two groups C 5 Relates subtraction to taking away	● add and subtract numbers of objects to 10 ● begin to add by counting on from the number of objects in the first set ● begin to know some addition facts, e.g. ● doubles of numbers to double 5	● can use apparatus to find totals of 10 ● is beginning to 'know' by deriving or memory some totals to 10 ● can find addition and subtraction with answers up to 5 with apparatus as an aid to calculation	*I know some pairs of numbers that total 10.* *I can use counters or blocks to add numbers with answers up to 5.*

Unit 1 ⬛ Securing number facts, understanding shape

Framework objectives	Assessment focuses		Success criteria for Year 1	Learning outcomes
	Foundation stage profile scale point	Level 1		
⑧ Sorting shapes ⑨ Pictures, models and patterns				
Visualise and name common 2D shapes and 3D solids and describe their features; use them to make patterns, pictures and models	SSM 4 Talks about, recognises and recreates simple patterns SSM 6 Uses language such as 'circle' or 'bigger' to describe the shape and size of solids and flat shapes	• use everyday language to describe properties of 2D and 3D shapes, e.g. • sort shapes and say how they have selected them • use properties such as large, small, triangles, roll, stack • begin to refer to some features of shapes such as side and corner • begin to name the shapes they use in the context of an activity	• can use 2D and 3D shapes to make patterns, pictures and models • can name most 2D and 3D shapes • recognises 2D and 3D shapes in the classroom and playground • is beginning to visualise a shape from a verbal description	*I can use 2D and 3D shapes to make patterns, pictures and models.* *I can name most of the 2D and 3D shapes I use in my work as well as those I see in my classroom and playground.* *I am beginning to picture a shape in my head.*

Activity ①

Prior learning
Children can use numbers or shapes to copy and continue a simple pattern.

Framework objective
Describe simple patterns and relationships involving numbers or shapes; decide whether examples satisfy given conditions

Vocabulary
count, double, pattern, repeating pattern, sort, property, set, group

Resources
Interactive activity: Domino pattern
Resource sheet: Self-assessment
Classroom resources: sets of dominoes

① Domino pattern

Provide each pair of children with a set of dominoes. Ask them to sort out the dominoes so that they make a pattern that begins with double zero and ends with double 6. When they have completed the pattern, show the children the interactive activity 'Domino pattern'. Together agree which domino goes where. Drag and drop the dominoes into place. Check which children completed the task, and who needs further support. Decide whether to use the self-assessment sheet for the children to record their achievements and what they need to do next.

Teacher support
Less confident learners: Complete the task as a group.
More confident learners: Challenge these children to make another pattern from the dominoes and to explain what they have done.

Common misconception
Children do not recognise a pattern.
Sort the dominoes together. Ask children to find the double zero and double 6. *Which domino do you think comes next? What number do you think goes at the top/bottom of the domino?* Elicit that each number will be 1, then 2, and so on. Place the dominoes in a line and ask children to point out what patterns they can see (both top numbers and bottom numbers run from 0 to 6). Repeat for another task, such as finding all the dominoes that have a 1, and making a pattern from them.

Probing questions
● Can you see a pattern in the number of objects? Is there a pattern in the shapes? How do you know what comes next?
● Can you talk about the pattern in your own words?

Next steps
Support: Provide another pattern puzzle, such as sorting all the dominoes with a zero and putting these into an order. See also Foundation Stage Overview of Learning 5 and 11.
Extension: Challenge these children to make other patterns with the dominoes. Ask them to explain their pattern, and how they decided to solve the problem. See also Year 1 Block B Unit 2.

BLOCK B

BLOCK B

Activity ②

Prior learning
Children can count at least 20 objects and know that the last number they say is how many there are altogether.

Framework objective
Count reliably at least 20 objects, recognising that when rearranged the number of objects stays the same; estimate a number of objects that can be checked by counting

Vocabulary
count, compare, order, estimate

Resources
Resource sheet: Self-assessment
Classroom resources: counting items (20 for each child), containers (for example, empty margarine tubs)

② How many items?

Ask the children to watch how many items (up to five) you put on the table. Without touching, count aloud how many there are. Ask the children to take a handful of their counting items, estimating eight. Encourage them to check their estimate by counting. Observe their counting. Do they coordinate the touch, count and move? Do they point and count? Repeat for quantities up to 20. *How many are there now? Do you need to count them again?* Decide whether to use the self-assessment sheet for the children to record their achievements and next steps. They can draw a few items, count them, and write the numeral.

Teacher support
Less confident learners: Limit the count to up to 6, then 8, and gradually extend the count over time. Check that the children coordinate the touch, count and move.
More confident learners: Encourage these children to point rather than touch, unless the items are in an irregular 'heap' on the table. Extend the estimate and count to beyond 20.

Common misconception
Children do not coordinate the touch, count and move.
Put five counters in a line. Ask children to count them. Observe their counting method. Do they touch each counter, say the number name, then move the counter to do the same for the next counter? Do they stop when they have counted the final one and say that number as the quantity of the set? If necessary, touch, count and move together, and emphasise the last number said. *How many are there? What was the last number that you said? So that number tells us how many there are.* Repeat.

Probing questions
● Spread out these ten counters that you put in a line. How many are there? How do you know?
● Can you count the cubes (up to five) without touching them?
● Make an estimate of the number of cubes in the jar. Is it near 10 or 20?

Next steps
Support: Provide opportunities for estimating counting within the classroom environment, such as collecting enough glue sticks for everyone sitting at the table to have one, and counting to check that all the glue sticks have been collected in again at the end of the lesson. Over time, extend the counting range to at least 20. See also Foundation Stage Overview of Learning 3.
Extension: Encourage these children to estimate how many with larger numbers. See also Year 1 Block A Unit 2.

Activity ③

BLOCK B

Prior learning
Children can read, write and order numbers up to 20.

Framework objective
Read and write numerals from 0 to 20, then beyond; use knowledge of place value to position these numbers on a number track and number line

Vocabulary
read, write, record

Resources
Resource sheets: Self-assessment, Numeral cards 0-10, Numeral cards 11-20
Classroom resources: whiteboards and pens

③ Numerals

Say to the children: *Write the number that is 1 more than 5, 1 less than 37, that comes between 5 and 9.* Check that the numeral is written correctly in each case. *You can make a number line with your boards. Sam, write 1 on your board and stand next to me. Jan, write the next number...* Continue until all the numbers to 20 are in place. Ask some of children to sit down. *Jon, say one of the missing numbers. Write it. Stand where it belongs.* Decide whether to use the self-assessment sheet for the children to record their achievements and what they need to do next. They can write some personal numbers (for example, their age, house number).

Teacher support
Less confident learners: Start with numbers to 10, extending to 20 over time.
More confident learners: Invite these children to extend the number line, writing numbers up to 30.

Common misconception
Children do not read or write numbers correctly, nor do they know where they belong in a number line.
Provide practice in reading and writing numbers, checking that children can form them correctly. Encourage children to play card games where they order a stack of shuffled numeral cards. Begin with numbers to 5, and then extend the range over time as confidence grows.

Probing questions
● What is the number before/after 10?
● What is the number before 20?
● What numbers are between 15 and 20?
● What number on the track is hidden?

Next steps
Support: Encourage the children to read and write numbers from around the classroom. They can play games with numeral cards, such as Snap or Pelmanism. See also Foundation Stage Overview of Learning 7.
Extension: Encourage these children to read, write and order numbers beyond 20, up to 30, then 40, and so on. See also Year 1 Block A Unit 2.

Activities ④ and ⑤

BLOCK B

Prior learning
Children can use counters or the number line/100-square to find the number that is one more or one less than a number. They can find the number that is 10 more or 10 less for a particular tens number.

Framework objective
Say the number that is 1 more or less than any given number, and 10 more or less for multiples of 10

Vocabulary
one more, one less, ten more, ten less

Resources
Interactive activity: Number line: 1 more, 1 less
Resource sheets: Numeral cards 0–10, Numeral cards 11–20, Numeral cards 21–30, 100-square, Self-assessment

④ Number line: 1 more, 1 less

Before the lesson, hide all but one of the numbers on the number line displayed on the first screen of the interactive activity 'Number line: 1 more, 1 less'. Reveal the screen and ask the children to say the numbers that are 1 more and 1 less than the number shown. Use the 'clear' button to reveal the hidden numbers one by one. Continue until the entire number line has been revealed. Check which children are answering correctly and confidently, and who needs more experience. Click on the second tab on the left-hand side of the screen to reveal a 0–20 number line that you can use to continue the activity with different numbers if you wish to do so. Decide whether to use the self-assessment sheet for the children to record their achievements and what they need to do next. They can write their own number line as part of their record.

Teacher support
Less confident learners: Begin with the numbers to 5, and extend over time to up to 10. Use numeral cards to build the number line.
More confident learners: Extend the number line to 20 and beyond. Use numeral cards to build the number line.

Common misconception
Children do not recognise the 1 more and 1 less numbers.
Practise counting from zero to 10 and back. Stop on, say, 6 and ask: *What number will we say next? So what is 1 more than 6? What number did we say just before 6? So what is 1 less than 6?* Repeat for other numbers. When children are confident with counting and recognising the one before and after a given number, try the activity again to check their confidence level.

Probing questions
● There are four counters in the pot. How many will there be if I put in one more?
● There are six spots on my dice. Imagine there is one less spot. How many spots would there be?

Next steps
Support: Over time, extend the number line to up to 10, then to 20. See also Foundation Stage Overview of Learning 2.
Extension: Decide whether to extend the range to beyond 20. See also Year 1 Block A Unit 2.

 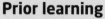

⑤ Ten more, ten less questions

Provide the resource sheet '100-square' for each child. Explain that you will ask a 'ten more' or 'ten less' question. The children can answer by putting up their hands. Ask: *What is the number that is 10 more/10 less than 20? Than 50? How can you find the answer on your number line?* Observe which children are answering confidently and who needs more experience. Decide whether to use the self-assessment sheet for the children to record their achievements and what they need to do next. They can record some 10 more and 10 less numbers as part of their record.

Teacher support
Less confident learners: Concentrate on 10 more and 10 less for numbers to 40, and then extend over time.
More confident learners: Challenge these children to explain in their own words to others in the class how they work out 10 more and 10 less numbers.

Common misconception
Children do not recognise the 10 more or 10 less numbers.
Begin by counting together from zero to 50 in tens. When children are confident with this, ask them to count again. Stop them on 40. *What is the next number that you will say? So what is 10 more than 40? What is the number before 40 that you said? So what is 10 less than 40?* Repeat this, extending the count to up to 100 over time.

Probing questions
● I am thinking of 30. What is 10 more/less than 30? How could a number line or 100-square help you?

Next steps
Support: Practise counting in 10s from zero to 100. Stop the count on, say, 50, and ask: *What is the next number that you will say? What was the number before 50?* Repeat frequently. Link this to finding the 10 more and 10 less numbers. See also Year 1 Block A Unit 1.
Extension: Build confidence with 10 more and 10 less than decade numbers to 100 through oral and mental starters that include counting tens, and finding the one before and one after any decade number to 100. See also Year 1 Block B Unit 2.

Activities ⑥ and ⑦

Prior learning

Children can begin to solve a problem or puzzle by deciding what the important information is. They know some pairs of numbers that total 10, and can use counters or blocks to add numbers with answers up to 5.

Framework objectives

- Solve problems involving counting, adding, subtracting, doubling or halving in the context of numbers, measures or money, for example to 'pay' and 'give change'
- **Derive and recall all pairs of numbers with a total of 10 and addition facts for totals to at least 5; work out the corresponding subtraction facts**

Vocabulary

problem, answer, method, add, equals

Resources

Resource sheet: Self-assessment
Classroom resources: counting items, interlocking cubes, empty margarine tub

⑥ Adding to 5

Say to the children: *Listen to this addition sentence, and then find a way to solve it. You can use any way you like to find the answer. What is 3 add 1? 2 add 3? How did you work out the answer? Who used a different way?* Praise particularly those children who worked mentally and ask them to explain their method. Encourage the others to use their counting items to model the mental method. *What numbers could you add to give a total of 5?* Decide whether to use the self-assessment sheet for the children to record their achievements and what they need to do next. They could record some of the addition sentences.

Teacher support

Less confident learners: Begin with addition to 3, with 1 + 2 and 2 + 1, using counting items. Encourage the children to count on from the first set rather than counting each set then counting all.
More confident learners: Encourage these children to work mentally to calculate small totals to 5.

Common misconception

Children do not count on from one group to the next in order to find the total. They count each group and then count all.
Put out three cubes and one cube. Ask children to find how many there are in total. Encourage them to count the three cubes, and then to count the one cube by counting on like this: *1, 2, 3 and 4. So 3 add 1 is 4.* Repeat for other small quantities with totals to up to 5.

Probing questions

- How are you going to tackle this?
- What is the important information that you have?
- What approach are you going to use? Why?
- What numbers could you add to give a total of 4? Are there other ways to get a total of 4?

Next steps

Support: Encourage the children to count on from the larger number each time in order to find a total. See also Foundation Stage Overview of Learning 8.
Extension: Encourage these children to work mentally, and to begin to know the answers to addition to 5. See also Year 1 Block B Unit 2.

⑦ Make a ten

Show the children ten counting items. Count them out together. Explain that you will hide some of the items under the empty margarine tub. Hide four and keep six in view. Ask the children to count how many are in view. *How many are there altogether? How many can you see? So how many are hidden under the pot? Yes, 4. Say the number sentence together: 6 + 4 = 10.* Repeat this for other 'hidings'. Invite the children to explain each time how they solved the puzzle. Decide whether to use the self-assessment sheet for the children to record their achievements and what they need to do next. They could record some of their addition sentences.

Teacher support
Less confident learners: Provide counting items so that the children can model the question for themselves, working in pairs.
More confident learners: Encourage these children to develop quick recall of these facts by limiting the time that they can take to find the answer.

Common misconception
Children do not have strategies for finding totals of 10.
Make a set of four and a set of six from interlocking cubes. *How many are in each set? How can we find out how many there are in total?* Suggest that children begin with the larger set (6) and count on for 4: *6 and 7, 8, 9, 10. So 6 + 4 = 10.* Suggest that if children find counting on difficult, they can keep a tally with their fingers. Check that they are counting on, not counting 1, 2, 3, 4. Repeat for other totals of 10.

Probing questions
- How are you going to tackle this?
- What is the important information that you have?
- What approach are you going to use? Why?
- If you know that 7 + 3 = 10, what else do you know?

Next steps
Support: Encourage the children to move to mentally counting on, keeping a tally with their fingers if necessary. See also Foundation Stage Overview of Learning 8.
Extension: Provide opportunities (for example, during oral and mental starters) for the children to recall the facts with a total of 10. See also Year 1 Block B Unit 2.

BLOCK B

Activities ⑧ and ⑨

BLOCK B

Prior learning
Children can use 2D and 3D shapes to make patterns, pictures and models. They can name most of the shapes they use in their work as well as those they see elsewhere. They are beginning to picture shapes in their heads. They can use numbers or shapes to copy and continue a simple pattern.

Framework objectives
● **Visualise and name common 2D shapes and 3D solids and describe their features; use them to make patterns, pictures and models**
● Describe simple patterns and relationships involving numbers or shapes; decide whether examples satisfy given conditions

Vocabulary
shape, make, build, draw, curved, straight, hollow, solid, flat, side, corner, point, face, edge, cuboid, pyramid, cone, cylinder, triangle, circle, rectangle, square

Resources
Resource sheet: Self-assessment
Classroom resources: paint, a set of 3D shapes in an opaque bag, a set of 2D shape tiles in an opaque bag

⑧ Sorting shapes

Sit in a circle with the children. Pass around the bag of 3D shapes. Each child puts their hand into the bag, feels a shape and names it. Then the child shows the shape to everybody. Ask questions about the shape such as (for a cube): *What shape is each face? How many faces does a cube have?* Repeat for the 2D shapes. Decide whether to use the self-assessment sheet for the children to record their achievements and what they need to do next. They could draw around the faces of a 3D shape, and of a tile, and write the shape names.

Teacher support
Less confident learners: Ask for just the name of the shape. Describe the shape's properties to the children, showing them each one carefully.
More confident learners: Encourage these children to say as many properties of shapes as they can think of.

Common misconception
Children cannot distinguish between 3D and 2D shapes.
Show children a cube and ask them to name it. Draw around it on some paper. *What shape has the cube made on the paper?* Agree that it is a square. Explain that the faces of the cube are square in shape. Repeat this for other shapes to produce rectangles (cuboid), circles (cone or cylinder), and triangles (triangular prism, and triangle-based pyramid). Children can use the shapes to stamp with paint onto paper. Ask them to name each 3D shape and the faces that it has.

Probing questions
● Picture a rectangle in your head. Tell me about it so that I can picture it too.
● When you imagine a square, how many edges does it have?
● Which shapes have you seen in the classroom/in the playground/on the way to school/at home?

Next steps
Support: Continue to make comparisons between 2D and 3D shapes so that the children are clear about the difference and understand that 3D shapes will have 2D shapes as their faces. See also Foundation Stage Overview of Learning 11.
Extension: Encourage the children to sort shapes by their properties. They can decide on the property for sorting. See also Year 1 Block B Unit 2.

⑨ Pictures, models and patterns

Provide 2D shape tiles and 2D models for the children to use. Ask them to place the shapes next to each other to make a picture or model (for example, a house or animal). They then make a repeating pattern with the shapes. This can be repeated over time so that the children have the opportunity to experience making pictures, models and repeating patterns with different 2D tiles. When they have finished, ask them to explain which shapes they have used, what they have made, and why they have used particular shapes. Decide whether to use the self-assessment sheet for the children to record their achievements and what they need to do next.

Teacher support
Less confident learners: Work with the children as a group, and encourage them to talk about what they are making with the shapes. Check that they know the shape names.
More confident learners: Challenge these children to make more complex pictures, models and patterns.

Common misconception
Children cannot copy or continue a pattern using shapes.
Make a simple ABAB pattern with shapes. Ask children to describe the pattern by saying the names of the shapes: *triangle, square, triangle, square. Which shape will go next in my pattern? And next?* Make a new simple pattern. Ask children to say what comes next, and next. Ask them to shut their eyes. Remove one piece from the pattern, and push the others together to close the gap. *What is wrong with this pattern?* Ask them to continue a simple ABAB pattern that you start for them.

Probing questions
● Is there a pattern in the shapes? How do you know what comes next?
● Can you talk about the pattern in your own words?
● What shapes have you used in your picture/model/pattern?
● Why did you choose these shapes?

Next steps
Support: Provide further opportunities for the children to make patterns, pictures and models with shapes. Encourage them to name the shapes, describe the patterns, and describe the properties of the shapes that they choose. See also Foundation Stage Overview of Learning 11.
Extension: Encourage these children to make and continue more complex patterns, choosing their own shapes. Invite them to describe what they have done to other children, referring to the shapes by their names. See also Year 1 Block B Unit 2.

Unit 2 ▢ Securing number facts, understanding shape

Introduction
In this unit children should be encouraged to work in pairs and groups, listen to each others' ideas and discuss what they will do. They explore shape and number patterns, describing the patterns. They solve problems, using the mathematics they are learning. They continue to recognise, describe and make patterns with shapes. They find the number that is one or ten more/less than a given number. They find and explore doubles of all numbers to 10. They continue to develop their skills in addition and subtraction.

Framework objectives	Assessment focuses		Success criteria for Year 1	Learning outcomes
	Foundation stage profile scale point	Level 1		
① One more, one less, ten more, ten less				
Say the number that is 1 more or less than any given number, and 10 more or less for multiples of 10	C 3 Finds one more or one less from a group of up to five objects C 7 Finds one more or one less than a number from 1 to 10	• order numbers to 10 • say what number comes next, is one more/less	• can say the number that is 1 more/less than a given number • can find the number that is 10 more/less than a given decade number	*I can say the number that is one more or one less than a number.* *I can say the number that is ten more or ten less than a multiple of 10.*
② Make 10 ③ Five				
Solve problems involving counting, adding, subtracting, doubling or halving in the context of numbers, measures or money, for example to 'pay' and 'give change'	C 8 Uses developing mathematical ideas and methods to solve practical problems	• solve addition/subtraction problems involving up to 10 objects, e.g. • given a number work out 'how many more to make…' • choose which of given pairs of numbers add to a given total • solve measuring problems such as how many balance with… • solve problems involving 1p or £1 coins	• recognises key words in a problem or puzzle • knows what the key words mean • can identify the mathematics required to solve the problem or puzzle from the key words	*I can use what it says in a problem to work out what sum to do.*
Derive and recall all pairs of numbers with a total of 10 and addition facts for totals to at least 5; work out the corresponding subtraction facts	C 4 Relates addition by combining two groups C 5 Relates subtraction to taking away	• add and subtract numbers of objects to 10 • begin to add by counting on from the number of objects in the first set • begin to know some addition facts, e.g. • doubles of numbers to double 5	• has mental strategies to find number pairs that total 10 • has mental strategies such as counting on to find totals up to 5 • is beginning to use mental strategies to find subtraction answers	*I know the pairs of numbers that total 10.* *I know how to add numbers to make different totals up to 5 and I am beginning to work out take away answers as well.*

Unit 2 ⬜ Securing number facts, understanding shape

Framework objectives	Assessment focuses		Success criteria for Year 1	Learning outcomes
	Foundation stage profile scale point	Level 1		
④ What's my double?				
Recall the doubles of all numbers to at least 10	C 4 Relates addition by combining two groups	● begin to know some addition facts, e.g. ● doubles of numbers to double 5	● uses strategies such as counting on to find doubles of numbers to 5 + 5 or more ● is beginning to 'know' some of the doubles to 5 + 5 or more	*I can recall or work out the doubles of numbers up to 5 + 5 or more.*
⑤ Picture a shape				
Visualise and name common 2D shapes and 3D solids and describe their features; use them to make patterns, pictures and models	SSM 4 Talks about, recognises and recreates simple patterns SSM 6 Uses language such as 'circle' or 'bigger' to describe the shape and size of solids and flat shapes	● use everyday language to describe properties of 2D and 3D shapes, e.g. ● sort shapes and say how they have selected them ● use properties such as large, small, triangles, roll, stack ● begin to refer to some features of shapes such as side and corner ● begin to name the shapes they use in the context of an activity	● knows the names of familiar 2D and 3D shapes ● can visualise the shapes	*I know the names of familiar 2D and 3D shapes and I can picture these shapes in my head.*
⑥ Repeating patterns ⑦ Number patterns for 5				
Describe simple patterns and relationships involving numbers or shapes; decide whether examples satisfy given conditions	SSM 4 Talks about, recognises and recreates simple patterns	● recognise and use a simple pattern or relationship, e.g. with support ● copy and continue a simple pattern of objects, shapes or numbers	● can make a simple pattern using numbers or shapes ● can describe their pattern to others	*I can use numbers or shapes to make patterns of my own.* *I can describe my patterns to others.*

Activity ①

BLOCK B

Prior learning
Children can say the number that is one more or one less than a number. They can say the number that is 10 more or 10 less than a multiple of 10.

Framework objective
Say the number that is 1 more or less than any given number, and 10 more or less for multiples of 10

Vocabulary
count to, count on/back to/from

Resources
Display page: One more, one less, ten more, ten less
Resource sheet: Self-assessment

① One more, one less, ten more, ten less

Reveal the display page 'One more, one less, ten more, ten less'. Say: *I will write a number onto the track. Tell me the 'one more' and 'one less' numbers. What is one more than 6?* Use the pen tool to write 7 on the track. *What is one less than 6?* Write 5. Repeat until the number track is complete. Now erase the numbers and write in the 12, so that the track begins this time with 11. Repeat until the number track is full. Repeat for ten more and ten less, beginning the number line with 10. Decide whether to use the self-assessment sheet for the children to record their achievements and what they need to do next.

Teacher support
Less confident learners: Concentrate on one more, one less.
More confident learners: Extend the one more, one less to beyond 20.

Common misconception
Children do not know the counting sequence for counting in ones or tens.
Practise counting in ones from 0 to 20. Ask children to stop counting when you say 'Stop'. Ask questions such as: *Which number did you just say? Which number comes next? Which number was one before that number?* Repeat this until children are confident with 'one more and one less' numbers. Repeat this for 'ten more and ten less' numbers, counting in tens from 0 to 100.

Probing questions
● What is one more than 18? One less than 15?
● Can you ask me a one more/less question? How will you know if my answer is right?
● I will clap where a number is missing. 22, 32, 42, [one clap], 62. What is the missing number?

Next steps
Support: Once the children are confident finding 'one more, one less' numbers up to 10, increase the range to 15 and then to 20. Introduce ten more and ten less. See also Year 1 Block A Unit 2.
Extension: Extend the range for 'one more and one less' numbers to 50, then beyond. See also Year 1 Block A Unit 3.

Activities ② and ③

Prior learning
Children can use what it says in a problem to work out what sum to do. They know the pairs of numbers that total 10. They know how to add numbers to make different totals up to 5 and they are beginning to work out take away answers as well.

Framework objectives
● Solve problems involving counting, adding, subtracting, doubling or halving in the context of numbers, measures or money, for example to 'pay' and 'give change'
● **Derive and recall all pairs of numbers with a total of 10 and addition facts for totals to at least 5; work out the corresponding subtraction facts**

Vocabulary
problem, answer, method, number sentence, sign, operation, add, plus, makes, sum, total, altogether, subtract, minus, take away, leaves, difference

Resources
Interactive activity: Make 10
Resource sheets: Numeral cards 0–10, Self-assessment
Classroom resources: counters, interlocking cubes, empty margarine tub

② Make 10

Reveal the interactive activity 'Make 10'. Play several rounds of bingo, providing the children with different cards each time. Ask some word problems about the facts, such as: *There are ten sweets in the bowl. Three sweets are eaten. How many sweets are left? Mandy has six cats. Susie has four cats. How many cats are there altogether?* Encourage children to explain how they worked out the answers. Praise in particular those who 'know' the facts. Decide whether to use the self-assessment sheet for the children to record their achievements and what they need to do next. They can write out the addition facts for 10, to show what they know.

Teacher support
Less confident learners: Provide counting aids (such as interlocking cubes) for the children to model the number sentences. Set the timer to 20 seconds.
More confident learners: Reduce the time to five seconds to check that the children now know these facts.

Common misconception
Children do not relate finding complements of 10 to counting on.
Explain that you will say a number. Ask children to find the number to add to it to make 10. Provide interlocking cubes so that children can count on. Say *7 and 8, 9, 10. How many did we count on? 3. So 7 add 3 is 10.* Repeat this for the other complements of 10. Encourage children to move to using a number line or track to count on, then to counting on mentally. At this stage they may find keeping a tally with their fingers helpful.

Probing questions
● Use the numeral cards 1 to 9. Which pairs of numbers total 10? What number would you add to 5 to make 10?
● Tell me about how you solved this problem.
● Why did you choose that calculation?

Next steps
Support: Encourage the children to use mental counting on. They can use their fingers to keep a tally if necessary. See also Year 1 Block B Unit 1.
Extension: Encourage these children to recall these facts quickly. Ask them to explain how they found the answer to any complements of 10 where they falter. See also Year 1 Block B Unit 3.

BLOCK B

③ **Five**

Hide one counter under the empty tub and leave four counters out. Ask: *How many counters can you see? So how many are under the tub? How did you work that out? Who just knew the answer? Say an addition sentence for the counters* (for example, 4 + 1 = 5) *and a subtraction sentence* (for example, 5 − 1 = 4). Repeat. Pose word problems such as: *Five birds sit on the roof. Four fly away. How many are left?* Decide whether to use the self-assessment sheet for the children to record their achievements and what they need to do next. Ask them to write some addition and subtraction sentences for 5.

Teacher support
Less confident learners: Provide counting items or a number line as aids to calculation.
More confident learners: Encourage the children to respond as quickly as possible to the questions to demonstrate their knowledge of addition and subtraction facts for totals up to 5.

Common misconception
Children do not have a strategy for finding totals or 'take aways' up to 5.
Ask: *What is 2 + 1? How can we find this total?* If children want to use cubes, encourage them to count on from the 2. Model this on the number line. Then model counting on mentally: *2 and 3. So 2 add 1 is 3.* Children may keep a tally with their fingers. Repeat for subtraction, counting up from the lower to the higher number: *What is 3 take away 1? We can count on from 1 to 3. Keep count with your fingers: 1 and 2, 3. So 3 take away 1 is 2.* Repeat.

Probing questions
● Tell me about how you solved this problem.
● Why did you choose that calculation?
● There are five beans. I hide some. I write this to show what I have done:
5 − 3 = 2. Hide a different number. Write a subtraction sentence to show what you have done.

Next steps
Support: Provide opportunities to practise recalling or calculating mentally for totals to 5. See also Year 1 Block B Unit 1.
Extension: Provide opportunities for these children to demonstrate that they know the answers for addition and subtraction to 5. Expect rapid recall of these facts. See also Year 1 Block B Unit 3.

Activity ④

BLOCK B

Prior learning
Children can recall or work out the doubles of numbers up to 5 + 5 or more.

Framework objective
Recall the doubles of all numbers to at least 10

Vocabulary
double, add, plus, equals, total

Resources
Worksheet: What's my double?
Classroom resources: 1-6 dice, blank dice, interlocking cubes

④ What's my double?

Ask the children to work in pairs. They each need a copy of the worksheet 'What's my double?' and a 1-6 dice. Invite them to take turns to toss the dice. They use the dice number to write a double sentence. For example, for a dice score of 3 they write 3 + 3 = 6.

Teacher support
Less confident learners: Use blank dice and write in 1, 1, 2, 2, 3, 3, so that the children practise doubles to 3. Extend this over time.
More confident learners: When the children are confident with doubles to at least 5, extend the range of doubles to 10. Use blank dice and write in 5, 6, 7, 8, 9, 10.

Common misconception
Children do not have a strategy for finding doubles.
Make two towers of two interlocking cubes. Say: *How many cubes are there in this tower? And how many cubes are there in that tower? So 2 add 2 is? Another way to say 2 add 2 is to say double 2. So double 2 is?* Repeat this for other examples using cubes then number lines. Encourage children to count on mentally. Over time expect them to commit these facts to memory.

Probing questions
● I roll double 3. What is my score?
● Pick a number and double it. What is the largest number you can double? Show how you know that your answer is right.

Next steps
Support: Gradually extend the range of numbers that the children can double mentally. Encourage them to model the doubling using cubes or number lines, then to work mentally, counting on. See also Year 1 Block E Unit 1.
Extension: Extend the range of numbers to 10 for the children to double. Discuss the strategies that they use to do this, and encourage them to begin to 'know' these facts. See also Year 1 Block E Unit 2.

Activity ⑤

Prior learning
Children know the names of familiar 2D and 3D shapes and they can picture these shapes in their heads.

Framework objective
Visualise and name common 2D shapes and 3D solids and describe their features; use them to make patterns, pictures and models

Vocabulary
shape, make, build, draw, curved, straight, hollow, solid, flat, side, corner, point, face, edge, cuboid, pyramid, cone, cylinder, triangle, circle, rectangle, square

Resources
Resource sheet: Self-assessment
Classroom resources: 2D shapes, 3D shapes, opaque bags, paint

⑤ Picture a shape

Say: *I will describe a shape. Try to picture it in your heads. Shut your eyes. Picture a square. Walk around the sides. How many sides are there? How many corners? What is special about the sides of a square?* (They are all the same length.) *Picture a rectangle. Walk around the rectangle. How many sides are there? How many corners? What is special about a rectangle?* (Opposite sides are the same length.) Repeat for 3D shapes. *Picture a cube. Walk around your cube. What shape are the faces?* Decide whether to use the self-assessment sheet for the children to record their achievements and what they need to do next. They can draw the shapes that they have 'seen'.

Teacher support
Less confident learners: These children may find it easier if they hold the shape in their hands while listening to the description. They can follow its outline with a finger and try to see that in their heads.
More confident learners: Ask these children to describe the shapes, and name some properties.

Common misconception
Children cannot differentiate between a square and a cube, nor a rectangle and a cuboid.
Put a cube into an opaque bag. Ask children to feel the cube inside the bag and describe what they feel. Take the cube out of the bag. *What shape is this? What shape are the faces of a cube?* Provide some paint and ask children to stamp each face of a cube onto some paper. *Describe the shapes that you see.* Repeat with a cuboid. Explain that squares and rectangles can be seen on solid shapes, and also as drawings or cut-outs.

Probing questions
● Picture a triangle in your head. Start at the top and walk around the sides of the triangle. How many sides do you walk around? How many corners does the triangle have?
● Use these small rectangles. How many different bigger rectangles can you make from them?

Next steps
Support: Encourage the children to imagine shapes without holding them in their hands. See also Year 1 Block B Unit 1.
Extension: Extend the range of 2D and 3D shapes that the children know and encourage them to explore their properties, such as sliding and rolling for 3D shapes. See also Year 1 Block B Unit 3.

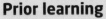

Activities ⑥ and ⑦

Prior learning
Children can use numbers or shapes to make patterns of their own. They can describe their patterns to others.

BLOCK B

Framework objective
Describe simple patterns and relationships involving numbers or shapes; decide whether examples satisfy given conditions

Vocabulary
pattern, puzzle, answer, right, wrong, what could we try next? how did you work it out?

Resources
Interactive activity: Repeating patterns
Worksheet: Number patterns for 5
Resource sheet: Self-assessment
Classroom resources: beads and laces

⑥ Repeating patterns

Show the children the interactive activity 'Repeating patterns'. Explain that the shapes on the screen can be used to make a repeating pattern. Ask the children to continue the pattern that you begin: square, circle, circle, square, circle, circle. Discuss what comes next. Invite children to say the next four or five items for the pattern. Now ask the children to suggest how a pattern might begin. Follow one of the children's suggestions, and continue it, with children saying what comes next. Repeat this several times. Decide whether to use the self-assessment sheet for the children to record their achievements and what they need to do next.

Teacher support
Less confident learners: Provide beads and laces. Make a simple pattern with the beads, such as red, blue, red, blue. Invite children to say what comes next. Repeat for other simple patterns.
More confident learners: Encourage these children to make more complex patterns, such as abcc, abcc, and so on.

Common misconception
Children cannot continue the pattern correctly.
Begin with a simple ABABAB pattern made from shapes. Ask children to say the pattern together. *Which shape will come next? How do you know that?* Place the pattern piece down in the pattern. *What comes next? And next?* Repeat this with other simple patterns, such as AABAAB.

Probing questions
● Describe the pattern so that your partner can make it.
● Tell me how to continue the pattern.
● Make a string of beads for me. First a red, then a blue. What colour is the sixth bead? What colour will the tenth bead be? The 20th bead? How do you know?

Next steps
Support: Provide further opportunities for the children to copy and continue patterns, gradually increasing the complexity of the patterns. See also Year 1 Block B Unit 1.
Extension: Ask these children to use shapes to invent their own patterns. Challenge them to make them more complex. They can continue each other's patterns. See also Year 1 Block B Unit 3.

⑦ Number patterns for 5

Ask the children to use the worksheet 'Number patterns for 5' to record addition sentences with a total of 5, and then subtraction sentences that begin 5 − □. Ask them to look carefully at the addition sentences. *How can we write these so that they make a pattern?* If children need help, suggest that they begin with 0 + 5, then 1 + 4 and so on. Ask them to write these in an order that makes a pattern. Repeat this with the subtraction sentences. Now invite the children to explain what they can see in the number sentence patterns.

Teacher support
Less confident learners: Work as a group to make the number patterns with these number sentences.
More confident learners: Challenge these children to choose another number, such as 7, and make addition totals of 7, and subtraction sentences that begin 7 − □ to make patterns.

Common misconception
Children do not recognise the number pattern.
Ask children to find number sentences with a total of 3. Write them in the order that children say them. *How can we put the number sentences in order?* If they are unsure, suggest that they start with 0 + 3. *Which number sentence will come next? Why?* Write the number sentences in order. Discuss the patterns: the first number increases by 1 and the second number decreases by 1 each time, in order to make the total of 3. Repeat this for subtractions that begin 3 − □.

Probing questions
● Which number sentence should go first? Why do you think that?
● Which one comes next? And next? Why is that?
● What patterns can you see? Say what is happening.

Next steps
Support: During an oral and mental starter, encourage the children to help to construct other similar patterns, such as additions with a total of 4. See also Year 1 Block B Unit 1.
Extension: Encourage these children to make other number patterns, such as additions with a total of 8. See also Year 1 Block B Unit 3.

■**SCHOLASTIC**

Unit 3 ▢ Securing number facts, understanding shape

Introduction
In this unit children should be encouraged to ask questions, answer questions, and to make suggestions and take turns. Throughout the unit they should be encouraged to solve problems and to describe simple patterns and relationships, such as addition and subtraction patterns, or those involving odd or even numbers or shapes. They continue to develop their skills in addition and subtraction, doubling, and in writing number sentences that are relevant to what they are doing. They sort shapes, recognise a set of shapes from a general statement and use data handling, such as a Carroll diagram, as a means of sorting clearly shapes or numbers.

Framework objectives	Assessment focuses		Success criteria for Year 1	Learning outcomes
	Foundation stage profile scale point	Level 1		
① Totals of 10 ② Add and subtract to 5				
Derive and recall all pairs of numbers with a total of 10 and addition facts for totals to at least 5; work out the corresponding subtraction facts	C 4 Relates addition by combining two groups C 5 Relates subtraction to taking away	● add and subtract numbers of objects to 10 ● begin to add by counting on from the number of objects in the first set ● begin to know some addition facts, e.g. ● doubles of numbers to double 5	● has mental strategies to find number pairs that total 10 ● 'knows' the number pairs that total 10 ● has mental strategies such as counting on to find totals up to 5 ● has mental strategies such as counting back to find subtraction answers to 5 ● 'knows' answers or some answers for addition and subtraction calculations for answers to 5	*I know the pairs of numbers that total 10.* *I can remember or work out simple add and take away calculations with answers to 5.*
③ Double up				
Recall the doubles of all numbers to at least 10	C 4 Relates addition by combining two groups	● begin to know some addition facts, e.g. ● doubles of numbers to double 5	● uses strategies such as counting on to find doubles of numbers to 10 + 10 ● 'knows' some of the doubles to 10 + 10	*I can recall doubles of numbers up to 10 + 10.*
④ Adding three numbers				
Solve problems involving counting, adding, subtracting, doubling or halving in the context of numbers, measures or money, for example to 'pay' and 'give change'	C 8 Uses developing mathematical ideas and methods to solve practical problems	● solve addition/subtraction problems involving up to 10 objects, e.g. ● given a number work out 'how many more to make...' ● choose which of given pairs of numbers add to a given total ● solve measuring problems such as how many balance with... ● solve problems involving 1p or £1 coins	● can explain how the puzzle or problem was solved using appropriate mathematical vocabulary	*I can talk about how I solved a problem or puzzle.*

Unit 3 Securing number facts, understanding shape

BLOCK B

Framework objectives	Assessment focuses		Success criteria for Year 1	Learning outcomes
	Foundation stage profile scale point	Level 1		
Relate addition to counting on; recognise that addition can be done in any order; use practical and informal written methods to support the addition of a one-digit number or a multiple of 10 to a one-digit or two-digit number	C 4 Relates addition by combining two groups	• understand addition as finding the total of two or more sets of objects • add and subtract numbers of objects to 10 • begin to add by counting on from the number of objects in the first set	• uses counting on strategies for adding • may use fingers to keep a tally of what has been counted on • understands that adding can be done in any order and the answer will be the same	*I can add using counting on.* *I know that if I add my numbers in any order I will get the same answer.*

(5) Taking away

Understand subtraction as 'take away' and find a 'difference' by counting up; use practical and informal written methods to support the subtraction of a one-digit number from a one-digit or two-digit number and a multiple of 10 from a two-digit number	C 5 Relates subtraction to taking away	• understand subtraction as 'taking away' objects from a set and finding how many are left	• can use taking away to find an answer to a subtraction question • can count up from the smaller number to find the difference between two numbers • may keep a tally of how many have been counted	*I can subtract by taking away and by counting up to find the difference between the numbers.*

(6) Number patterns (7) Match a shape (8) Shape patterns

Describe simple patterns and relationships involving numbers or shapes; decide whether examples satisfy given conditions	SSM 4 Talks about, recognises and recreates simple patterns	• recognise and use a simple pattern or relationship, e.g. with support • copy and continue a simple pattern of objects, shapes or numbers	• can make a pattern using numbers or shapes • can describe what comes next in the pattern	*I can use numbers or shapes to make patterns of my own and explain what comes next.*

(6) Number patterns

Use the vocabulary related to addition and subtraction and symbols to describe and record addition and subtraction number sentences	C 6 In practical activities and discussion, begins to use the vocabulary involved in adding and subtracting	• record their work, e.g. • record their work with objects, pictures or diagrams • begin to use the symbols '+' and '=' to record additions	• uses appropriate mathematical vocabulary to describe addition and subtraction calculations • uses appropriate symbols when writing a number sentence (+, −, =)	*I can use mathematical words and symbols to describe and record add and take away calculations.*

■ SCHOLASTIC

Unit 3 ⬜ Securing number facts, understanding shape

Framework objectives	Assessment focuses		Success criteria for Year 1	Learning outcomes
	Foundation stage profile scale point	Level 1		
⑦ Match a shape ⑧ Shape patterns				
Visualise and name common 2D shapes and 3D solids and describe their features; use them to make patterns, pictures and models	SSM 4 Talks about, recognises and recreates simple patterns SSM 6 Uses language such as 'circle' or 'bigger' to describe the shape and size of solids and flat shapes	• use everyday language to describe properties of 2D and 3D shapes, e.g. ● sort shapes and say how they have selected them ● use properties such as large, small, triangles, roll, stack ● begin to refer to some features of shapes such as side and corner ● begin to name the shapes they use in the context of an activity	• recognises the properties of shapes using such features as sides, corners and faces • can work with a partner to picture a shape as it is described	*I can describe and match a shape using mathematical features such as sides, corners, faces. I can work with a partner to picture a shape in my mind.*
⑨ Shape sort				
Use diagrams to sort objects into groups according to a given criterion; suggest a different criterion for grouping the same objects	SSM 2 Sorts or matches objects and talks about sorting SSM 8 Uses developing mathematical ideas and methods to solve practical problems NLC 8 Uses developing mathematical ideas and methods to solve practical problems	• draw simple conclusions from their work, e.g. with support ● describe the different ways they have sorted objects, what is the same about objects in a set, how sets differ • sort and classify objects, e.g. ● sort using one criterion or sort into disjoint sets using two simple criteria such as boy/girl or thick/thin ● sort objects again using a different criterion • represent their work, e.g. ● use the objects they have sorted as a record ● use objects/pictures to create simple block graphs	• can choose appropriate criteria for sorting into groups • can use simple sorting diagrams to place objects appropriately • can regroup objects by a different criterion	*I can choose reasons for sorting my objects into groups and use a diagram to record this. I can use the same objects but group them using different reasons.*

Activities ① and ②

BLOCK B

Prior learning
Children know the pairs of numbers that total 10. They can remember or work out simple add and take away calculations with answers to 5.

Framework objective
Derive and recall all pairs of numbers with a total of 10 and addition facts for totals to at least 5; work out the corresponding subtraction facts

Vocabulary
add, plus, makes, sum, total, altogether, subtract, minus, take away, leaves, difference

Resources
Resource sheets: Numeral cards 0–10, Self-assessment
Classroom resources: whiteboards and pens

① Totals of 10

Give each pair of children a set of 0–10 numeral cards and ask them to shuffle them. They should then take turns to turn over the top card, and say the number that adds to their card number to make 10. Their partner can challenge the answer if they do not agree. They then check their answer (for example, by counting on in ones to 10 to find the missing number). Observe the children to see who 'knows' the answer, and who is still using a mental strategy. Decide whether to use the self-assessment sheet for the children to record their achievements and what they need to do next. They can record some of their number sentences to demonstrate what they know.

Teacher support
Less confident learners: Play the game together. Ask the children to say a number sentence each time (for example: *6 add 4 equals 10*).
More confident learners: Challenge these children to play the game as quickly and accurately as they can.

Common misconception
Children do not know the complements of 10.
Play the game again, this time asking children to explain how they can find the answer. For the moment encourage using cubes, or a number line, or counting and keeping track by using fingers. Ask children to say the number sentence each time so that they become familiar with this. Repeat the game over time, gradually removing the cubes, then number lines, then the use of fingers, so that children do recall the answers.

Probing questions
● How many different pairs of numbers can you remember that have a total of 10? How can you be sure you have got them all?

Next steps
Support: Provide opportunities to practise recalling these facts. See also Year 1 Block A Unit 2.
Extension: Challenge the children to find all the addition sentences that total 20. Ask them to find a way to order their results and then to explain the patterns that they see. See also Year 2 Block A Unit 1.

② Add and subtract to 5

Say: *I will ask some addition or subtraction questions that use the numbers up to 5.* When you say *Show me,* children should hold up their whiteboards for you to see their answers. Begin with very easy questions such as: *What is 2 add 1? How much is 3 add 2? What is the total of 4 and 1?* Move to subtraction sentences such as: *What is 3 subtract 1? What is 4 take away 2? What is the difference between 5 and 2?* Decide whether to use the self-assessment sheet for the children to record their achievements and what they need to do next. They can record some of their number sentences.

Teacher support
Less confident learners: Limit the activity to addition number sentences. Observe how the children find the answers, and suggest strategies where they do not know the answer.
More confident learners: Keep the pace sharp for these children. Check whether they can find the subtraction answers quickly.

Common misconception
Children cannot find the answers to the subtraction questions, so do not understand the link between addition and subtraction.
Ask: *What is 3 add 1? What is 1 add 3?* Write both addition sentences on the board. Write 4 − 3 and 4 − 1 and ask children to find the answers. Discuss how each of these number sentences uses the numbers 1, 3 and 4. Explain that if children know the addition sentence, they can use this to find the subtraction answer. Repeat for another trio of numbers, such as 2, 3, 5.

Probing questions
● Look at this addition: 2 + 3 = 5. Can you make a subtraction sentence using those numbers?

Next steps
Support: Remind children how they can use the addition facts that they know to help them to find the subtraction answers. Say, for example: *What is 4 + 1? So what is 5 take away 1? How did you work that out?* Repeat this for other pairs of addition and subtraction number sentences. See also Year 1 Block B Unit 2.
Extension: When the children are confident with recall of both addition and subtraction facts to up to 5, extend the number range to up to 10. See also Year 2 Block A Unit 1.

BLOCK B

Activity ③

BLOCK B

Prior learning
Children can recall doubles of numbers up to 10 + 10.

Framework objective
Recall the doubles of all numbers to at least 10

Vocabulary
double

Resources
Worksheet: Double up

③ Double up

Ask the children to complete the worksheet 'Double up'. They find the doubles of the numbers 1 to 10, and join each number to its double.

Teacher support
Less confident learners: Decide whether to work as a group to find the answers. Ask: *How did you work out the answers if you do not 'know' them?*
More confident learners: Challenge these children to work from 1, then 2 (and so on), finding each double in order.

Common misconception
Children have difficulty finding doubles of the numbers 1 to 10.
Begin with numbers up to 5. Write the numbers on the board and, as children find the doubles, write them underneath like this:

1	2	3	4	5
2	4	6	8	10

Ask: *What do you notice about the double numbers?* Agree that these are all even and that they begin the counting in 2s from 0 pattern. If children really struggle to remember these doubles, suggest that they count on their fingers in 2s. Extend this to doubles for 6 to 10 in the same way.

Probing questions
● If you choose a number between 1 and 10 and double it, what is your answer? Can you double other numbers? Try these: 10, 20, 30, 40, 50.
● I doubled a number and got 18. What number did I double?

Next steps
Support: Provide plenty of opportunities for recalling or finding by mental methods the doubles of numbers to 10. Include this regularly as part of an oral and mental starter. See also Year 1 Block E Unit 2.
Extension: Extend finding doubles to numbers 11 to 20 and beyond. See also Year 1 Block E Unit 3.

Activity ④

Prior learning
Children can add using counting on. They know that if they add their numbers in any order they will get the same answer. They can talk about how they solved a problem or puzzle.

Framework objectives
● Solve problems involving counting, adding, subtracting, doubling or halving in the context of numbers, measures or money, for example to 'pay' and 'give change'
● Relate addition to counting on; recognise that addition can be done in any order; use practical and informal written methods to support the addition of a one-digit number or a multiple of 10 to a one-digit or two-digit number

Vocabulary
add, plus, makes, sum, total, altogether, problem, answer, method, number sentence, sign, operation, explain, read, write, record

Resources
Resource sheet: Self-assessment

BLOCK B

④ Adding three numbers

Write 4, 5, 6, 7, 8, 9 on the board. Explain that you would like the children to add three of the numbers. They should write a number sentence to show what they have done and work out the answer mentally. Ask them to repeat this three times, choosing different numbers. Pose word problems such as: *There are four cats, two dogs and five rabbits in the garden. How many animals is that altogether? How did you solve the problem?* Decide whether to use the self-assessment sheet for the children to record their achievements and what they need to do next. They can write some of their number sentences to demonstrate what they have achieved.

Teacher support
Less confident learners: Limit the activity to choosing just two numbers each time to total.
More confident learners: Challenge these children to choose four numbers each time.

Common misconception
Children do not recognise that it does not matter in which order numbers are added.
Write 3, 2, 1 and ask: *What is 3 add 2 add 1? How did you work that out? So what is 3 add 1 add 2? Or 1 add 2 add 3? Does it matter in which order we add numbers?* Repeat this for other additions of three numbers such as 2, 3, 4, until children are confident with the fact that the order in which numbers are added does not make a difference to the answer.

Probing questions
● How did you do the calculations? What if you used different numbers, would that change your way of working?
● I want to total these numbers: 2, 14 and 8. Tell me some different ways I could add them. Would they all give the same answer? How do you know?

Next steps
Support: Provide further experience of adding two single-digit numbers, then three. See also Year 1 Block A Unit 3.
Extension: Encourage these children to total four single-digit numbers. See also Year 2 Block A Unit 3.

BLOCK B

Activity ⑤

Prior learning
Children can subtract by taking away and by counting up to find the difference between the numbers. They can talk about how they solved a problem or puzzle.

Framework objective
Understand subtraction as 'take away' and find a 'difference' by counting up; use practical and informal written methods to support the subtraction of a one-digit number from a one-digit or two-digit number and a multiple of 10 from a two-digit number

Vocabulary
subtract, minus, take away, leaves, how many?, how many more to make...?, problem, answer, method, number sentence, sign, operation, explain, read, write, record

Resources
Worksheet: Taking away
Resource sheets: Numeral cards 0-10, Numeral cards 11-20
Classroom resources: counters (20 for each pair of children), interlocking cubes

⑤ Taking away

Say to the children: *In pairs, take turns to put some counters in the empty box on the worksheet 'Taking away'. Your partner counts how many there are. The first child takes some counters away and places them outside the box. The other child counts what is left. Then write a subtraction sentence.* For 15 counters and 8 taken away, the children would write: 15 − 8 = 7. Ask the children to repeat this with different numbers of counters, until they have each written ten subtraction sentences.

Teacher support
Less confident learners: For these children, reduce the number of counting items to ten or fewer.
More confident learners: Challenge the children to repeat the activity, this time taking two number cards from a stack of 0–20, or more.

Common misconception
Children are not confident about when to stop counting when taking away. Make a tower of six cubes. Explain that two cubes have been taken away. Ask children to count up with you to find how many cubes there were to begin with. Say: *6 and 7, 8. So 8 take away 2 is 6.* If children need further help, suggest that they count up keeping a tally with their fingers. Repeat for other quantities.

Probing questions
● Show me two numbers that have a difference of 3. Show me another pair of numbers with a difference of 3.
● How many do I add on to get from 3 to 8?
● 15 ducks are on the pond. 11 of them go away. How many are left?

Next steps
Support: Gradually increase the start number for subtraction to up to 20. See also Year 1 Block A Unit 3.
Extension: Encourage the children to explain how they solved subtraction problems. See also Year 2 Block A Unit 1.

Activity ⑥

Prior learning
Children can use mathematical words and symbols to describe and record add and take away calculations. They can use numbers to make patterns of their own and explain what comes next.

Framework objectives
● **Use the vocabulary related to addition and subtraction and symbols to describe and record addition and subtraction number sentences**
● Describe simple patterns and relationships involving numbers or shapes; decide whether examples satisfy given conditions

Vocabulary
subtract, minus, take away, leaves, difference, how many?, how many more to make...?, how many more is... than...?, how much more is...?, how many fewer is... than...?, how much less is...?, what is the difference between...?

Resources
Resource sheet: Self-assessment

⑥ Number patterns

Ask the children to work in pairs. Ask them to write down all the addition and subtraction sentences which use the number 10 (for example, 4 + 6 = 10, 18 − 8 = 10). Explain that no number in the subtraction sentence can be more than 20. Ask the children to find a way to order their addition sentences, then their subtraction sentences. Invite them to discuss with their partner the patterns that they can see. Decide whether to use the self-assessment sheet for the children to record their achievements and what they need to do next.

Teacher support
Less confident learners: Limit the activity to numbers within 10.
More confident learners: Challenge the children to find more than one pattern for addition, and for subtraction.

Common misconception
Children cannot use the vocabulary of addition and subtraction to describe patterns.
Write '0 + 10 = 10' and '1 + 9 = 10' on the board. *What comes next? And next?* Complete the pattern to 10 + 0 = 10. Ask children to describe a pattern that they can see. For example, that the first number increases by 1 each time, and the second number decreases by 1 each time. Repeat this for another pattern, such as 10 − 0 (and so on). Encourage children to use the vocabulary to explain the patterns that they see.

Probing questions
● Make a different pattern using the same numbers. What comes next?
● There are 12 pegs on a coat hanger. Five are showing. How many are hidden under the cloth? What number sentence could we write to show this?
● Put numbers in the shapes to make the sentence true: □ + △ = 12.

Next steps
Support: Ask the children to re-write other number sentences in order, such as additions with a total of 16: 0 + 16; 1 + 15 and so on. Encourage them to explain the patterns that they can see. See also Year 1 Block A Unit 3 and Block B Unit 2.
Extension: Challenge the children to explore other number patterns, and to explain the patterns to the class (for example, adding an even number to 17 to give 17 + 2, 17 + 4, and so on). See also Year 2 Block B Unit 1.

Activities ⑦ and ⑧

BLOCK B

Prior learning
Children can use shapes to make patterns of their own and explain what comes next. They can describe and match a shape using mathematical features such as sides, corners, faces. They can work with a partner to picture a shape in their minds.

Framework objectives
● Describe simple patterns and relationships involving numbers or shapes; decide whether examples satisfy given conditions
● **Visualise and name common 2D shapes and 3D solids and describe their features; use them to make patterns, pictures and models**

Vocabulary
problem, answer, method, explain, read, write, record, order, estimate, predict, pattern, repeating pattern, shape, make, build, draw, curved, straight, hollow, solid, flat, side, corner, point, face, edge, cuboid, pyramid, cone, cylinder, triangle, circle, rectangle, square

Resources
Interactive activity: Shape patterns
Resource sheet: Self-assessment
Classroom resources: 2D shape tiles, 3D shapes, opaque bags (one for each pair), paint, sets of triangle, circle and square shape tiles

⑦ Match a shape

Ask the children to work in pairs. They will need a set of 2D shape tiles placed in an opaque bag. They take turns to choose a shape, then, without showing their partner, they describe the shape. Their partner says the name of the shape. The other child then shows the shape to confirm that it has been correctly named. Repeat this for 3D shapes. Decide whether to use the self-assessment sheet for the children to record their achievements and what they need to do next. They can draw some of their shapes on the sheet.

Teacher support
Less confident learners: Work as a group. Encourage the children to use the vocabulary of shape to describe the shapes accurately.
More confident learners: Challenge these children to describe new shapes, such as pentagons, hexagons and octagons. Introduce the name vocabulary for these shapes.

Common misconception
Children cannot differentiate between 3D and 2D shapes (for example, they confuse a rectangle and a cuboid).
Put a cube into an opaque bag. Ask children to feel the cube inside the bag and describe what they feel. Take the cube out of the bag. *What shape is this? What shape are the faces of a cube?* Provide some paint and ask children to stamp each face of a cube onto some paper. Ask them to describe the shapes that they see. Repeat this with a cuboid. Explain that squares and rectangles can be seen on solid shapes, drawings or cut-outs.

Probing questions
● Think of a shape. Without saying its name, describe it so that I can find your shape in the box.
● Describe your shape to your partner so that your partner can picture it.
● Draw a line on this square to make two triangles. Use a ruler.

Next steps
Support: Include shape recognition during oral and mental starters. For example: *I am thinking of a shape. It is a flat shape. It has four straight sides. All the sides are the same length. What is my shape?* See also Year 1 Block B Unit 1.

Extension: Encourage the children to take the lead during an oral and mental starter, as outlined in Support. They must think of the clues. They may find this difficult at first, so ask them to prepare some descriptions for a shape beforehand. See also Year 2 Block B Unit 1.

⑧ Shape patterns

Reveal the interactive activity 'Shape patterns'. Ask the children to look carefully at the pattern on the first screen. Ask: *What is wrong with this? What is missing?* Invite children to drag and drop the correct shapes to complete the pattern. Repeat for screens 2 and 3. On screen 4 the children have the opportunity to drag and drop the on-screen shapes to form patterns of their own on the blank grid. Decide whether to use the self-assessment sheet for the children to record their achievements and what they need to do next. If appropriate, provide each child with a set of triangle, circle and square shape tiles which they can draw around in order to show their patterns.

Teacher support
Less confident learners: Simplify the pattern that the children re-arrange, such as just squares and triangles.
More confident learners: Challenge these children to make up their own pattern, using at least three different shapes.

Common misconception
Children do not recognise what constitutes a pattern.
Use two different shape tiles, such as triangles and squares. Set these out: triangle, square, triangle, square, and so on. *Let's say the shapes together.* Point to the shapes as you say: *triangle, square, triangle, square… What is the pattern? What is the next shape in the pattern? And the next?* Repeat this with another arrangement. Then make a pattern but miss out a shape. *I have a shape left over from this pattern. Where does it belong? How do you know that?* Repeat until children are confident.

Probing questions
● Can you make a different pattern using the same shapes?
● What comes next? How did you work that out?
● Look at these shapes. Which two of the shapes would fit together to make this shape [a pentagon]? Tick the two shapes.

Next steps
Support: Provide further opportunities to copy and repeat patterns, to make further patterns from the same shapes, and to identify the missing shape in a pattern. See also Year 1 Block B Unit 2.
Extension: Encourage the children to make more complex patterns, then to use the same shapes to make other patterns. See also Year 2 Block B Unit 3.

BLOCK B

Unit 3 Securing number facts, understanding shape

Activity ⑨

Prior learning
Children can choose reasons for sorting objects into groups and use a diagram to record this. They can use the same objects but group them using different reasons.

Framework objective
Use diagrams to sort objects into groups according to a given criterion; suggest a different criterion for grouping the same objects

Vocabulary
shape, make, build, draw, curved, straight, hollow, solid, flat, side, corner, point, face, edge, cuboid, pyramid, cone, cylinder, triangle, circle, rectangle, square

Resources
Resource sheets: Carroll diagram, Venn diagram, Self-assessment
Classroom resources: sets of shapes for sorting (either 2D or 3D shapes)

⑨ Shape sort

Hand out the resource sheets 'Venn diagram' and 'Carroll diagram' and give each child a set of shapes. The children should decide in pairs how to sort their shapes, and then place them on the Carroll diagram. They can either draw around the shapes or sketch them to show their sorting. Ask them to write a heading for each of the sections, such as 'Four sides', 'Not four sides'. Ask the children to repeat this with another set of shapes and the Venn diagram. They can attach their completed resource sheets to the self-assessment sheet to provide evidence of their achievements.

Teacher support
Less confident learners: Work as a group. Ask the children to suggest how to sort the shapes. If they are unsure, then suggest 'Circles', 'Not circles'.
More confident learners: Challenge these children to be more adventurous in their sorting - for example, using 'Has rectangular face', 'Does not have rectangular face'.

Common misconception
Children do not understand how to sort using a negative property, such as does/does not have.
Put out some shapes. *How can we sort these?* Write the children's suggestions on a Carroll or Venn diagram. Write the 'does not...' or 'is not...' in the other section. Sort out the shapes together and place them on the diagram. *What is special about these shapes?* [Point to the positive property section.] Repeat this for the 'does not'/'is not' section. Ensure that children understand that anything that cannot fit in the positive section must go into the other section. Repeat for another sorting.

Probing questions
● How have you sorted the objects? How did you decide that this object belongs here?
● Could you sort them in a different way?
● One of these shapes is in the wrong place. Which shape is it? How do you know?

Next steps
Support: Encourage the children to decide upon their own criteria for sorting. See also Year 1 Block C Unit 2.
Extension: Challenge children to invent more complex sorting criteria and to explain these to their partner, then to the class. See also Year 1 Block C Unit 3.

■SCHOLASTIC

Units 1, 2 & 3 ◖ Periodic assessment

These activities can be used at the end of this block to assess those children that you think have achieved the objectives.

Addition and subtraction facts

Objective
Derive and recall all pairs of numbers with a total of 10 and addition facts for totals to at least 5; work out the corresponding subtraction facts

Assessment focus
Level 1: Begin to know some addition facts, e.g. doubles of numbers to double 5
Foundation stage profile scale points: Relates addition by combining two groups. Relates subtraction to taking away

Learning outcomes
● I know some pairs of numbers that total 10.
● I can use counters or blocks to add numbers with answers up to 5.
● I know the pairs of numbers that total 10.
● I know how to add numbers to make different totals up to 5 and I am beginning to work out take away answers as well.
● I can remember or work out simple add and take away calculations with answers to 5.

There are three activities for this objective.

1. Pairs of numbers that total 10: Provide the worksheet 'Addition and subtraction facts' and ask the children to find the pairs that total 10. If they are unsure, provide some counting apparatus or a number line to help them. This activity can be repeated over time until children demonstrate that they know the number pairs.
2. Addition to 5: This activity is best carried out in a small group. Decide whether the children need counting items or can calculate mentally. Begin with addition to a total of 3: 0 + 3, 1 + 2, 2 + 1, 3 + 0. Put out the relevant counters, such as 2 and ask: *How many more do I need to make 3?* Repeat this for the other addition sentences. Repeat for additions with a total of 4, then 5. Note how the children calculate the answers.
3. Subtraction up to 5: Begin with a given amount of counters, such as 4. Count these together. Explain that some of the counters have been hidden under the margarine tub. *Show what is left. How many counters are hidden?* Repeat this for other amounts up to 5. Note how the children calculate the answers. Decide whether to use the self-assessment sheet for the children to record their achievements and what they need to do next. They can write some of the number sentences that they know.

Adding and subtracting

Objective
Visualise and name common 2D shapes and 3D solids and describe their features; use them to make patterns, pictures and models

Assessment focus
Level 1: Use everyday language to describe properties of 2D and 3D shapes, e.g. sort shapes and say how they have selected

Learning outcomes
● I can use 2D and 3D shapes to make patterns, pictures and models.
● I can name most of the 2D and 3D shapes I use in my work as well as those I see in my classroom and playground.
● I am beginning to picture a shape in my head.
● I know the names of familiar 2D and 3D shapes and I can picture these shapes in my head.
● I can describe and match a shape using mathematical features such as sides, corners, faces.
● I can work with a partner to picture a shape in my mind.

(continued overleaf)

BLOCK B

Adding and subtracting (continued)

them; use properties such as large, small, triangles, roll, stack; begin to refer to some features of shapes such as side and corner; begin to name the shapes they use in the context of an activity
Foundation stage profile scale points: Talks about, recognises and recreates simple patterns. Uses language such as 'circle' or 'bigger' to describe the shape and size of solids and flat shapes

There are three parts to this activity. These can all be used together, or over several days.

1. Work with a small group of about six to eight children. Place 2D shape tiles into a bag, letting the children see each tile as it goes in. Now explain that you are going to ask the children to pass the bag from one child to the next. They should each find a shape tile, feel it carefully to recognise its shape, then say its name and show everyone the tile. Check that the children say the names correctly. Repeat this for 3D shapes.
2. Repeat the activity. This time, ask the children to describe the shape that they feel so that the other children can build the shape mentally until they know its name.
3. Ask the children to work with a partner. They take turns to describe a shape so that their partner pictures the shape in their mind, and names it. Decide whether to use the self-assessment sheet for the children to record their achievements and what they need to do next. They can sketch some of the shapes that they have described.

Addition and subtraction

Objective
Use the vocabulary related to addition and subtraction and symbols to describe and record addition and subtraction number sentences

Assessment focus
Level 1: Understand addition as finding the total of two or more sets of objects. Understand subtraction as 'taking away' objects from a set and finding how many are left
Foundation stage profile scale points: In practical activities and discussion, begins to use the vocabulary involved in adding and subtracting

Learning outcome
● I can use mathematical words and symbols to describe and record add and take away calculations.

Provide the worksheet 'Addition and subtraction'. Ask the children to write the answers to the word problems. Discuss the problems with the children and ask them to explain how they solved them. Check that the vocabulary that they use includes relevant mathematical words. Check that their recording is appropriate.

Name   Date

Addition and subtraction facts

🔲 Find two numbers that make a total of 10.

🔲 Join them with a line.

2

9

8

5

5

4

3

7

6

1

How easy?

Red
Amber
Green

How do you think you have done?

_____

_____

BLOCK B

BLOCK B

Name	Date

Addition and subtraction

◼ Write a number sentence and the answer to each problem.
Tell your teacher how you solved the problems.

1. Pat has 11 marbles in his pocket.
He puts 7 of them in a tub.
How many marbles are in his pocket?

_____

2. Mia has 14 stickers.
She gives Asha 8 of her stickers.
How many stickers does Mia have left?

_____

3. Sara buys a lolly for 16p.
She gives the shopkeeper 20p.
How much change does she get?

_____

_____

4. Sam spills paint on his number sentence. Write three answers
for this.

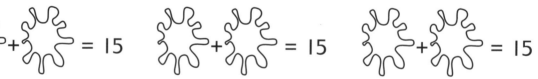

How easy?

Red

Amber

Green

How do you think you have done?

_____

_____

BLOCK C
Handling data and measures

Expected prior learning
Check that children can already:
- describe solutions to practical problems, drawing on experience, talking about their own ideas, methods and choices
- sort familiar objects and count how many objects share a particular property, presenting results using pictures, drawings or numerals
- count reliably at least ten everyday objects and recognise the corresponding numerals
- use language such as 'more' or 'less' to compare two numbers
- use language such as 'circle' or 'bigger' to describe the shape and size of solids and flat shapes
- use language such as 'greater', 'smaller', 'heavier' or 'lighter' to compare quantities

Objectives overview
The text in this diagram identifies the focus of mathematics learning within the block.

Key aspects of learning
- Enquiry
- Problem solving
- Information processing
- Communication

Collecting, organising, presenting and interpreting information to answer questions

Communicating findings

Representing information with practical resources, pictures, tables, block graphs or pictograms

Choosing and using appropriate units of measurement and measuring equipment

BLOCK C: Handling data and measures

Sorting information on a diagram using one criterion

Using ICT

Measuring and comparing lengths, weights and capacities using uniform non-standard and standard measures

Unit 1 ⬜ Handling data and measures

Introduction
During this unit, encourage children to discuss their work and explain what choices they made and why, speaking in an audible voice for all to hear. They sort objects and information, in order to help them to answer a question, and display their results using simple data collection charts and using pictures or objects to display their data. Encourage them to use the data to answer questions that you pose, and to begin to pose their own questions. They use data handling techniques to record information in their work on measures.

Framework objectives	Assessment focuses		Success criteria for Year 1	Learning outcomes
	Foundation stage profile scale point	Level 1		
① Heavier or lighter? ② How much does it hold? ③ Animal sort				
Estimate, measure, weigh and compare objects, choosing and using suitable uniform non-standard or standard units and measuring instruments (e.g. a lever balance, metre stick or measuring jug)	SSM 7 Uses language such as 'greater', 'smaller', 'heavier' or 'lighter' to compare quantities	• measure and order objects using direct comparison • compare lengths directly and put them in order • respond to and use the language of comparison: longer, longest, shorter, shortest, more, less, heavier, lighter	• can make direct comparisons of lengths, weights, capacities of more than two objects • can demonstrate that they know how to make a direct comparison by length, weight or capacity, using equipment appropriately • can order the objects by their length, weight or capacity	*I can compare the lengths/ weights/ capacities of more than two objects and put them in order.*
① Heavier or lighter?				
Answer a question by selecting and using suitable equipment, and sorting information, shapes or objects; display results using tables and pictures	SSM 2 Sorts or matches objects and talks about sorting SSM 8 Uses developing mathematical ideas and methods to solve practical problems	• draw simple conclusions from their work, e.g. with support • describe the different ways they have sorted objects, what is the same about objects in a set, how sets differ • identify which set has most, which object is biggest, smallest, tallest, etc • explain numbers and calculations, how many altogether, how many used or hidden, how many left, how many each, etc	• uses equipment appropriately	*I can answer a question using the equipment my teacher uses.*
② How much does it hold?				
Describe ways of solving puzzles and problems, explaining choices and decisions orally or using pictures	SSM 8 Uses developing mathematical ideas and methods to solve practical problems	• represent their work with objects or pictures • discuss their work, e.g. with support • respond to questions and ideas from peers and adults • refer to the materials they have used and talk about what they have done, patterns they have noticed, etc	• can use appropriate vocabulary to talk about how a problem was solved	*I can talk about how I solved a problem.*

Unit 1 📖 Handling data and measures

Framework objectives	Assessment focuses		Success criteria for Year 1	Learning outcomes
	Foundation stage profile scale point	Level 1		
③ Animal sort				
Use diagrams to sort objects into groups according to a given criterion; suggest a different criterion for grouping the same objects	SSM 2 Sorts or matches objects and talks about sorting	• sort and classify objects, e.g. ◦ sort using one criterion or sort into disjoint sets using two simple criteria such as boy/girl or thick/thin ◦ sort objects again using a different criterion ◦ sort objects into a given large scale Venn or Carroll diagram • represent their work, e.g. ◦ use the objects they have sorted as a record ◦ use objects/pictures to create simple block graphs	• can sort objects onto a large diagram • can make decisions about where objects go on the diagram • can give some explanation of why a particular item belongs in a specific place on the diagram	*I can sort objects by placing them onto a big diagram.*
④ Let's vote				
Answer a question by recording information in lists and tables; present outcomes using practical resources, pictures, block graphs or pictograms	SSM 2 Sorts or matches objects and talks about sorting	• use mathematics as an integral part of classroom activities, e.g. with support ◦ engage with practical mathematical activities involving sorting, counting and measuring by direct comparison ◦ begin to understand the relevance of mathematical ideas to everyday situations by using them in role-play	• can help to make a picture or chart • can read information from a chart or picture • can interpret the information in a picture or chart • uses appropriate vocabulary to explain what was found out	*I can help to answer a question and to show what we found out.*

Activity ①

Prior learning
Children can answer a question using the equipment their teacher uses. They can compare the weights of more than two objects and put them in order.

Framework objectives
● Answer a question by selecting and using suitable equipment, and sorting information, shapes or objects; display results using tables and pictures
● **Estimate, measure, weigh and compare objects, choosing and using suitable uniform non-standard or standard units and measuring instruments (e.g. a lever balance, metre stick or measuring jug)**

Vocabulary
problem, question, explain, predict, collect, organise, compare, order, sort, group, same, different, property, represent, interpret, count, tally, vote, measure, guess, heavy, light, heavier, heaviest, lighter, lightest

Resources
Resource sheet: Self-assessment
Classroom resources: bag of sand, balance scales, classroom items that are heavier than, lighter than, and about the same weight as the bag of sand

① Heavier or lighter?

This activity is best suited to a group of six to eight children working with a teacher or learning support assistant. Ask the children to find out which of the items provided are heavier or lighter than the bag of sand and to find a way to record their results (for example, in a table or by making a diagram using pictures). As the children set about solving the problem, observe how they decide to proceed, and how they decide to record their results. Decide whether to use the self-assessment sheet for the children to record their achievements and next steps. They can record their results on the back of the sheet.

Teacher support
Less confident learners: If the children are unsure about how to record their results, make a group chart to show results (for example, pictures comparing two items, with arrows to show 'is heavier than' or 'is lighter than').
More confident learners: Challenge these children to order the weights from lightest to heaviest.

Common misconception
Children do not understand how to use a two-pan balance to make comparisons of weight.
Explain to children that they are going to discover how to find which is lighter or heavier of two objects, using a balance. Place one item in one pan, and the other item in the second pan. *What has happened to the pans? Which one do you think shows the heavier item? Why do you think that? So which is lighter? How can you tell?* Observe together that the heavier item makes the pan go down, and the lighter item's pan is higher.

Probing questions
● How could you find out which objects are heavier than the bag of sand? What did you use to find out?
● Which of these three objects do you think will be the lightest? Which do you think will be the heaviest? Which will you compare first?

Next steps
Support: Provide further opportunities for comparing weights and finding which are heavier, which lighter, then extend to the heaviest and lightest. See also Foundation Stage Overview of Learning 13.

▷

> **Extension:** Challenge the children to find objects in the classroom that they estimate are heavier or lighter than an object such as a book. Ask them to make a diagram to show all the comparisons of the items that they have chosen. See also Year 1 Block C Unit 2.

Activity ②

Prior learning
Children can talk about how they solved a problem. They can compare the capacities of more than two objects and put them in order.

Framework objectives
- Describe ways of solving puzzles and problems, explaining choices and decisions orally or using pictures
- **Estimate, measure, weigh and compare objects, choosing and using suitable uniform non-standard or standard units and measuring instruments (e.g. a lever balance, metre stick or measuring jug)**

Vocabulary
problem, question, explain, predict, collect, organise, compare, order, sort, group, same, different, property, represent, interpret, count, tally, vote, measure, guess, full, half full, empty, holds, container

Resources
Resource sheet: Self-assessment
Classroom resources: containers (three with different capacities, two more with different capacities again), water or sand for filling and pouring

② How much does it hold?

This activity is best suited to a group of six to eight children working with a teacher or learning support assistant. Ask the children to compare how much three different containers hold and to put the containers in order of their capacity. Observe how they decide to carry out the task. Decide whether to use the self-assessment sheet for the children to record their achievements and what they need to do next. They can record the order of capacity from least to most using pictures and arrows.

Teacher support
Less confident learners: Encourage the children to use capacity vocabulary and to explain how they know that one container holds more/less than another.
More confident learners: Challenge these children to take two more containers and compare their capacities with the other containers, placing all five containers in order, starting with 'holds least'.

Common misconception
Children believe that the taller the container, the more it will hold.
Choose two containers that have different heights; the shorter should hold more than the taller. Ask: *How can we find out which holds more?* Compare their capacities by pouring. Discuss the fact that it is not possible to tell from the container's height how much it holds. Repeat with other containers, until children understand that height does not give a helpful estimate of capacity. Encourage them to look at height, width and depth of the containers when making an estimate of how much they hold.

Probing questions
- What else will you have to do to check if you have put them in order from lightest to heaviest?
- How could you show someone else that this one holds most?

BLOCK C

▷ **Next steps**
Support: Provide further opportunities for children to compare capacities. Over time, move from finding 'holds more/less' to comparing three or more containers to find which holds least/most. See also Foundation Stage Overview of Learning 13 and 14.
Extension: Ask children to explain to others how they how they made estimates of capacity, then checked this by pouring. Ask them to explain what they look for when making an estimate of capacity. See also Year 1 Block C Unit 2.

Activity ③

Prior learning
Children can compare the lengths of more than two objects and put them in order. They can sort objects by placing them on a big diagram.

Framework objectives
● **Estimate, measure, weigh and compare objects, choosing and using suitable uniform non-standard or standard units and measuring instruments (e.g. a lever balance, metre stick or measuring jug)**
● Use diagrams to sort objects into groups according to a given criterion; suggest a different criterion for grouping the same objects

Vocabulary
length, width, height, depth, size, long, short, tall, high, low, wide, narrow, deep, shallow, thick, thin, comparatives such as longer/longest, problem, question, explain, predict, collect, organise, compare, order, sort, group, same, different, property, represent, interpret, count, tally, vote

Resources
Interactive activity: Animal sort
Resource sheet: Self-assessment
Classroom resources: beanbag, large Carroll diagram on sugar paper, with the headings 'Wider than the beanbag' and 'Not wider than the beanbag', shoebox

③ Animal sort

Reveal the Carroll diagram on screen 1 of the interactive activity 'Animal sort'. Say: *Sort the animals using the diagram to show which are taller or shorter than a lion. Where do the animals go on the chart? Why?* Repeat for the Venn diagram on screen 2. Encourage discussion about the size of pets (ask: *How short is a puppy? How tall is your cat?*) and place the animals on the diagram only after you have discussed and agreed the positioning of the animals as a group. Ask the children to work in groups of eight. Invite them to compare their handspans: they draw around their own handspan (partners can help), cut out the outline, and write their name on it. *Work together to sort your handspans using the chart. Compare them with the beanbag. Estimate before you compare with the beanbag.* Decide whether to use the self-assessment sheet for the children to record their achievements and what they need to do next.

Teacher support
Less confident learners: Check that the children understand 'wider'. If they are unsure how to make a direct comparison, demonstrate this.
More confident learners: Ask these children to be ready to explain how they made their estimates and direct comparisons, and to explain their handspan chart to the rest of the class.

Common misconceptions
Children do not understand how to make direct comparisons of length.
Choose some classroom objects to compare. Discuss with children how to make

a direct comparison. Check that they understand that both items must have a starting point for comparing length. Pick up two objects. Hold one higher in the air and ask: *Which is longer?* Some children may interpret this as 'Which is higher?' Place both on the table so that they can make a direct comparison.

Probing questions
- How have you sorted the objects?
- Which of the objects on the diagram is wider than your handspan?
- Which are narrower? How do you know that?

Next steps
Support: Repeat the activity for other comparisons of length, such as height. Check that the children understand how to make the comparisons. See also Foundation Stage Overview of Learning 13 and 14.
Extension: Challenge these children to make their own simple Carroll or Venn diagram to sort, using the criteria 'Is deeper than the shoebox' and 'Is not deeper than the shoebox'. Ask them to find items in the classroom (such as containers) to make their comparisons, and to complete the diagram. See also Year 1 Block C Unit 2.

Activity ④

BLOCK C

Prior learning
Children can help to answer a question and to show what they found out.

Framework objective
Answer a question by recording information in lists and tables; present outcomes using practical resources, pictures, block graphs or pictograms

Vocabulary
problem, question, explain, predict, collect, organise, compare, order, sort, group, same, different, property, represent, interpret, count, tally, vote, measure, guess

Resources
Resource sheet: Self-assessment
Classroom resources: coloured pens or crayons, interlocking cubes, large sheet of paper

④ Let's vote

Explain to a group of about eight children that you would like them to answer a question as a group. Ask questions such as: *Which is your favourite ice-cream flavour? Make a block graph of your results. How will you solve the problem?* Notice who contributes during discussion and who is silent. The children might make a data collection chart for different flavours. If necessary, write the chart headings, but ask the children for suggestions as to what to write. They can make a block graph using the large sheet of paper and cubes. Again, help with labelling the graph if necessary, but ask the children what to write. Decide whether to use the self-assessment sheet for the children to record their achievements and what they need to do next.

Teacher support
Less confident learners: Work closely with these children, recording for them. If necessary, make suggestions about what they could do.
More confident learners: Let these children work without adult assistance. Afterwards, ask them to explain what they did and the decisions that they made.

Unit 1 Handling data and measures

Common misconceptions
Children do not know how to show the data that they have collected.
Ask: *How many pets do we have? How shall we find out? How could we record our results?* Make a data collection chart and record their results on this. Demonstrate how to use the data in their chart to make a block graph. Write the headings, but ask children to make towers of blocks to sit on the graph. *How many cats are there? How many dogs? Which is the most/least popular pet? How do you know? How many more cats/dogs are there than fish/hamsters? How can you tell?*

Probing questions
- What did you decide to do?
- How did you make your data collection chart?
- If you add your brick to that tower, what does that mean? Without counting, which of the flavours had most votes? How do you know?
- How many more/fewer ___ are there than ___?

Next steps
Support: Provide further examples of block graphs for the children to interpret. This could be part of an oral and mental starter. See also Foundation Stage Overview of Learning 6 and 14.
Extension: Invite these children to explain how they solve problems, record their data and make graphs. Invite them to say what they can tell from their results. See also Year 1 Block C Unit 2.

Unit 2 ⬛ Handling data and measures

Introduction

In this unit, encourage children to listen attentively and to follow instructions accurately. They develop their data-handling skills by answering a question, both for handling data activities and for measuring ones. They choose how to record their results, working in groups and coming to a decision about this. They develop their skills in measuring, again finding the answer to questions. This involves them in making decisions about how to carry out the task and about how to record their work.

Framework objectives	Assessment focuses		Success criteria for Year 1	Learning outcomes
	Foundation stage profile scale point	Level 1		
① Jug fill ② How wide is the classroom? ③ How much does it weigh?				
Estimate, measure, weigh and compare objects, choosing and using suitable uniform non-standard or standard units and measuring instruments (e.g. a lever balance, metre stick or measuring jug)	SSM 7 Uses language such as 'greater', 'smaller', 'heavier' or 'lighter' to compare quantities	• measure and order objects using direct comparison • compare lengths directly and put them in order • respond to and use the language of comparison: longer, longest, shorter, shortest, more, less, heavier, lighter • check which of two objects is heavier/lighter and begin to put three objects into order • find objects that are longer/shorter than a metre, heavier/lighter than 500 grams, hold more/less than 1 litre	• estimates before measuring • understands how to use the equipment appropriately for measuring lengths, weights and capacities • is beginning to use metre sticks to measure longer lengths	*I can use equipment to measure objects.*
① Jug fill				
Answer a question by selecting and using suitable equipment, and sorting information, shapes or objects; display results using tables and pictures	SSM 2 Sorts or matches objects and talks about sorting SSM 8 Uses developing mathematical ideas and methods to solve practical problems	• represent their work with objects or pictures	• can use equipment appropriately • can make a chart or table of the results that is clear and easy to understand	*I can show what I found out so that other people will understand.*
② How wide is the classroom?				
Describe ways of solving puzzles and problems, explaining choices and decisions orally or using pictures	SSM 8 Uses developing mathematical ideas and methods to solve practical problems	• discuss their work, e.g. with support • respond to questions and ideas from peers and adults • refer to the materials they have used and talk about what they have done, patterns they have noticed, etc.	• can use appropriate vocabulary to talk about how a problem was solved • can explain clearly why they chose to solve the problem in that way	*I can talk about why I chose to solve the problem in the way that I did.*

Unit 2 ◻ Handling data and measures

Framework objectives	Assessment focuses		Success criteria for Year 1	Learning outcomes
	Foundation stage profile scale point	Level 1		
③ How much does it weigh?				
Answer a question by recording information in lists and tables; present outcomes using practical resources, pictures, block graphs or pictograms	SSM 2 Sorts or matches objects and talks about sorting	● represent their work, e.g. ● use the objects they have sorted as a record ● use objects/pictures to create simple block graphs	● can draw a picture or chart ● can read information from a chart or picture ● can interpret the information in a picture or chart ● can use appropriate vocabulary to explain what was found out	*I can draw pictures/ diagrams to show what I have found out.*
④ Sort it!				
Use diagrams to sort objects into groups according to a given criterion; suggest a different criterion for grouping the same objects	SSM 2 Sorts or matches objects and talks about sorting	● sort and classify objects, e.g. ● sort using one criterion or sort into disjoint sets using two simple criteria such as boy/girl or thick/thin ● sort objects again using a different criterion ● sort objects into a given large scale Venn or Carroll diagram ● represent their work, e.g. ● use the objects they have sorted as a record ● use objects/pictures to create simple block graphs ● demonstrate the criterion they have used, e.g. ● respond to questions about how they have sorted objects and why each object belongs in a set ● talk about which set has most, for example 'most children stayed at school for lunch' ● talk about how they have represented their work	● can sort objects onto a large diagram which the children draw themselves ● can make decisions about where objects go on the diagram ● can give some explanation of why a particular item belongs in a specific place on the diagram	*I can sort objects using my own diagram to help me.*

Activity

Prior learning
Children can show what they found out so that other people will understand. They can use equipment to measure objects.

Framework objectives
● Answer a question by selecting and using suitable equipment, and sorting information, shapes or objects; display results using tables and pictures
● **Estimate, measure, weigh and compare objects, choosing and using suitable uniform non-standard or standard units and measuring instruments (e.g. a lever balance, metre stick or measuring jug)**

Vocabulary
problem, question, explain, predict, pattern, collect, organise, compare, order, sort, group, same, different, represent, interpret, count, tally, vote, measure, weigh, guess, information, graph, block graph, diagram, list, table, label, title, full, half full, empty, holds, container, measuring jug, capacity

Resources
Resource sheet: Self-assessment
Classroom resources: jugs, containers, cups, spoons, scoops, sand or water for filling, writing materials

① Jug fill

Provide filling and pouring materials and paper for recording results. Ask the children to work in pairs. *Decide how to find out how much these containers hold. You can use this equipment and decide how to record your results.* Observe the children as they work and note if one child in a pair takes little or no part in decision making. Decide whether to use the self-assessment sheet for the children to record their achievements and what they need to do next. They can use writing or pictures to show what they did.

Teacher support
Less confident learners: Work as a group. Encourage the children to suggest what to do, using relevant mathematical vocabulary.
More confident learners: Provide a simple data-processing program and ask the children to enter their data into a block graph. They could answer questions about it during the plenary.

Common misconception
Children do not understand that in order to make a comparison they must use the same uniform non-standard or standard units.
Provide a container and two different uniform non-standard units, such as an eggcup and a yogurt pot. *How many full eggcups/full yogurt pots will fill the container? Do you have the same number of eggcups as pots? Why do you think the numbers are different?* Ask children to pour a full eggcup into the yogurt pot. *What do you notice?* Agree that they hold different amounts, so it is important always to use the same uniform non-standard unit.

Probing questions
● Which container do you think will hold most? How many cups of water do you think it will take to fill the biggest jug?
● How do you know how much the biggest jug holds?
● What information did you need? What equipment did you use?

Next steps
Support: Provide further opportunities to estimate and measure capacity, using a variety of non-standard uniform units. See also Year 1 Block C Unit 1.
Extension: Encourage the children to measure capacity using litres. See also Year 1 Block C Unit 3.

BLOCK C

Activity ②

Prior learning
Children can talk about why they chose to solve the problem in the way that they did. They can use equipment to measure objects.

BLOCK C

Framework objectives
- Describe ways of solving puzzles and problems, explaining choices and decisions orally or using pictures
- **Estimate, measure, weigh and compare objects, choosing and using suitable uniform non-standard or standard units and measuring instruments (e.g. a lever balance, metre stick or measuring jug)**

Vocabulary
problem, question, explain, predict, pattern, collect, organise, compare, order, sort, group, same, different, property, represent, interpret, count, tally, vote, measure, weigh, guess, information, graph, block graph, list, table, label, title, unit, centimetre (cm), metre (m), ruler, metre stick, tape measure

Resources
Resource sheet: Self-assessment
Classroom resources: rulers, metre sticks, tape measure ten metres (+) long

② How wide is the classroom?

Ask a group of eight or ten children to work in pairs. Explain that you would like them to decide how to find out how wide the classroom is. Give them a couple of minutes to discuss what they are going to do and to make an estimate. *What is your estimate of the width? What units did you decide to use? Why did you decide to use a metre stick?* Ask them to write down their estimate, and then measure the width of the classroom, using their chosen units. Decide whether to use the self-assessment sheet for the children to record their achievements and what they need to do next.

Teacher support
Less confident learners: Watch how children measure. They may need help with using a metre stick or tape measure.
More confident learners: Suggest that children use the tape measure. Observe how they do this and whether they can confidently take a measurement in metres.

Common misconception
Children lack confidence in using metric measures.
Use a metre stick. *How long do you think that bookcase is? Tell me in metres.* Show children the metre stick so that they have a visual image of the measure. Now ask them to measure the book case. Observe how they set about the task and if necessary help them to measure more accurately. They may need help to see that they need to keep a finger where the end of the metre stick was in order to place it again.

Probing questions
- Which unit did you use? Why?
- Which measuring equipment did you use? Why?
- Did you make a good estimate?
- How many metres wide do you think the hall is? Write your guess on a piece of paper.

Next steps
Support: Provide further opportunities to use the metre in estimating measurements, such as estimating the height of the door, the length of the classroom, and so on. See also Year 1 Block C Unit 1.
Extension: Challenge these children to measure more accurately, such as by using half metres. See also Year 1 Block C Unit 3.

Activity ③

Prior learning
Children can draw pictures/diagrams to show what they have found out. They can use equipment to measure objects.

Framework objectives
- Answer a question by recording information in lists and tables; present outcomes using practical resources, pictures, block graphs or pictograms
- Estimate, measure, weigh and compare objects, choosing and using suitable uniform non-standard or standard units and measuring instruments (e.g. a lever balance, metre stick or measuring jug)

Vocabulary
problem, question, explain, predict, pattern, collect, organise, compare, order, sort, group, same, different, property, represent, interpret, count, tally, vote, measure, weigh, guess, information, graph, block graph, pictogram, diagram, list, table, label, title, balance, scales

Resources
Worksheet: How much does it weigh?
Resource sheet: Empty pictogram
Classroom resources: items for balancing/weighing, two-pan balance scales

③ How much does it weigh?

Ask children to work in pairs. Explain that you would like them to estimate the weight of three items, and then check by weighing, using the same uniform non-standard units for each item. They should record these results in the data collection chart on the worksheet 'How much does it weigh?' Provide also the resource sheet 'Empty pictogram' for children to complete. Explain that they should choose their own units, and then make a pictogram to show their results.

Teacher support
Less confident learners: Ask the children to hold an item in their hands, and then their chosen unit. Encourage them to make a reasonable guess about how many of the unit will balance the item.
More confident learners: Ask these children to explain why they chose a unit.

Common misconception
Children do not understand that they need to use the same uniform non-standard weights in order to weigh something.
Compare two different uniform non-standard weights by placing one in one pan and one in the other. Discuss how children can observe they weigh different amounts. Use one of the units to weigh something. Repeat using the other unit. Discuss how it is important to use the same unit for weighing something because all of those units weigh the same amount.

Probing questions
- How many cubes balanced the tennis ball? How did you know when you had found the correct weight?
- What does one weight on your pictogram stand for?
- How could you use your pictogram to find out which item you weighed was the heaviest/lightest?

Next steps
Support: Give further opportunities for children to estimate and then weigh items. Encourage them to record their results firstly in a data collection chart, and then in a diagram such as a pictogram. See also Year 1 Block C Unit 1.
Extension: Decide whether to provide other weights, such as 200g, and ask children to weigh items in grams. Decide whether to provide a scale and ask children to read the weight from the scale. See also Year 1 Block C Unit 3.

Activity ④

Prior learning Children can sort objects using their own diagram to help them.	**Framework objective** Use diagrams to sort objects into groups according to a given criterion; suggest a different criterion for grouping the same objects **Vocabulary** problem, question, explain, predict, pattern, collect, organise, compare, order, sort, group, same, different, property, represent, interpret, count, tally, vote, information, graph, block graph, pictogram, diagram, list, table, label, title **Resources** **Resource sheets:** Empty block graph, Empty pictogram, Self-assessment

④ Sort it!

Ask the children to work in groups of eight to ten. Say: *We are going to collect some data, sort it, and then display it using a chart, block graph or pictogram. Ask the others in your group what their favourite vegetable is. Make a chart to collect the data. Now make a pictogram or block graph with your data.* Show the children the resource sheets 'Empty block graph' and 'Empty pictogram' – they could use these to make their diagrams. Decide whether to use the self-assessment sheet, which could be attached to the children's written work as evidence of achievement.

Teacher support
Less confident learners: Work with these children as a group and make group charts and graphs.
More confident learners: Challenge these children to write a sentence about their results, such as which vegetable was most popular and how they know that from their chart.

Common misconception
Children do not understand how to transfer their data from a data collection chart to a block graph or pictogram.
Collect data, such as children's favourite colours. Make a data collection chart together, with children suggesting what to do. Show an empty pictogram. *What shall we write here? What data do we need?* Discuss how, if three children choose red, then three red icons are drawn on the pictogram. Repeat for a block graph. Display all three charts. Ask children to point out where the data is in the first chart and where it has been transferred to the others.

Probing questions
● How did your diagram help you to sort the information?
● What does your diagram tell you?
● Which has more/fewer votes than ___? How do you know?

Next steps
Support: Provide further opportunities for the children to collect, sort and record data, such as shoe size, number of letters in first name, and so on. Ask them questions about the data to check that they can interpret it. See also Year 1 Block C Unit 1.
Extension: Set a challenge such as collecting the data from all of the children in the class, and deciding how to sort a larger amount of data. See also Year 1 Block C Unit 3.

Unit 3 🟦 Handling data and measures

Introduction

In this unit, children are encouraged to work in small groups, agree how to carry out tasks and make decisions about recording. They answer questions involving handling data by selecting equipment, sorting and recording their results in tables and pictures. They describe carefully the decisions they made and their results. Children recognise the standard units of metre, litre and kilogram, and use smaller standard units which measure in centimetres, grams and milligrams. They plan together in small groups to carry out measuring and sorting tasks and decide on how to record and feed back to the others in the class.

Framework objectives	Assessment focuses		Success criteria for Year 1	Learning outcomes
	Foundation stage profile scale point	Level 1		
① Capacity compare	**② Length compare**	**③ Sorting lengths**	**④ Sorting weights**	**⑤ Talk about it!**
Estimate, measure, weigh and compare objects, choosing and using suitable uniform non-standard or standard units and measuring instruments (e.g. a lever balance, metre stick or measuring jug)	SSM 7 Uses language such as 'greater', 'smaller', 'heavier' or 'lighter' to compare quantities	● measure and order objects using direct comparison ● compare lengths directly and put them in order ● respond to and use the language of comparison: longer, longest, shorter, shortest, more, less, heavier, lighter ● check which of two objects is heavier/lighter and begin to put three objects into order ● find objects that are longer/shorter than a metre, heavier/lighter than 500 grams, hold more/less than 1 litre	● can estimate lengths and capacities by looking, and weights by feeling ● can measure using non-standard uniform units ● can record the measurements correctly ● can compare estimates and measurements in order to improve the accuracy of their estimates and to check that the measurements appear appropriate	*I can estimate by looking and feeling.* *I know how to measure objects, giving the measurements correctly.*
① Capacity compare				
Answer a question by selecting and using suitable equipment, and sorting information, shapes or objects; display results using tables and pictures	SSM 2 Sorts or matches objects and talks about sorting SSM 8 Uses developing mathematical ideas and methods to solve practical problems	● draw simple conclusions from their work, e.g. with support ● describe the different ways they have sorted objects, what is the same about objects in a set, how sets differ ● identify which set has most, which object is biggest, smallest, tallest, etc.	● can make choices about which equipment to use and can explain why that choice was made ● can decide how to record what is found out ● can use their written record to help explain their answer	*I can make choices about how to organise what I find out to help me to explain my answer.*
② Length compare				
Describe ways of solving puzzles and problems, explaining choices and decisions orally or using pictures	SSM 8 Uses developing mathematical ideas and methods to solve practical problems	● represent their work, e.g. ● use the objects they have sorted as a record ● use objects/pictures to create simple block graphs	● can make a diagram or draw a picture to show how the problem was solved ● can talk about the diagram or picture and explain what they found out	*I can draw a picture/diagram to show how I solved the problem.*

Unit 3 ▢ Handling data and measures

Framework objectives	Assessment focuses		Success criteria for Year 1	Learning outcomes
	Foundation stage profile scale point	Level 1		
③ Sorting lengths ④ Sorting weights ⑤ Talk about it!				
Answer a question by recording information in lists and tables; present outcomes using practical resources, pictures, block graphs or pictograms	SSM 2 Sorts or matches objects and talks about sorting	● represent their work, e.g. ● use the objects they have sorted as a record ● use objects/pictures to create simple block graphs	● can make a block graph using one icon for each item ● can label the block graph appropriately ● can interpret the block graph	*I can show what I found out by using a block graph.*
Use diagrams to sort objects into groups according to a given criterion; suggest a different criterion for grouping the same objects	SSM 2 Sorts or matches objects and talks about sorting	● sort and classify objects, e.g. ● sort using one criterion or sort into disjoint sets using two simple criteria such as boy/girl or thick/thin ● sort objects again using a different criterion	● can sort items, then re-sort by a different criterion ● can use information from comparing lengths or from balancing the items in order to sort the items	*I can sort objects in different ways.* *I can use what I know from comparing their lengths or balancing them.*

■ SCHOLASTIC

BLOCK C

Activity ①

Prior learning

Children can make choices about how to organise what they find out to help them to explain their answer. They can estimate by looking and feeling. They know how to measure objects, giving the measurements correctly.

Framework objectives
- Answer a question by selecting and using suitable equipment, and sorting information, shapes or objects; display results using tables and pictures
- **Estimate, measure, weigh and compare objects, choosing and using suitable uniform non-standard or standard units and measuring instruments (e.g. a lever balance, metre stick or measuring jug)**

Vocabulary
problem, question, explain, predict, pattern, collect, organise, compare, order, sort, group, same, different, property, represent, interpret, count, tally, vote, measure, guess, container, measuring jug, capacity, holds more than, holds less than, comparatives such as holds more/holds most

Resources
Worksheet: Capacity compare
Classroom resources: containers of different capacities, 1 litre jugs, filling/pouring materials (sand or water, spoons, scoops, eggcups, yogurt pots)

① Capacity compare

Put out a selection of five containers labelled A to E, and a range of units for capacity (including a litre jug). Ask the children to work in pairs. They should decide which will be the best unit and why, and then estimate and measure the capacities of all five containers. They can record their data on the worksheet 'Capacity compare'. Ask them to order the containers by capacity, from 'holds least' to 'holds most'. They can draw a diagram to show the ordering of the containers on the back of the worksheet.

Teacher support
Less confident learners: Limit the number of containers to three.
More confident learners: Ask the children to devise their own recording sheet and to make their comparisons using the litre jug.

Common misconception
Children do not make good estimates of capacity.
Show children a container, a scoop and some sand or water. *How many scoopfuls of sand do you think this container will hold?* Let children handle both the container and the scoop, and ask them to make an estimate. Ask a child to put scoopfuls of sand into the container until it is full. Ask another child to write a tick for each scoopful of sand. *How many scoopfuls of sand did we need to fill the container? Did you make a good estimate?* Repeat this for other containers.

Probing questions
- Why did you organise the information in that way? How does it help you to show that the bottle holds less than the jug?
- Did you think the jug or the mug would hold more? How much more?
- What did you do to measure carefully?

Next steps
Support: Provide further experience of estimating and measuring capacity, and of recording results. If children have difficulty in counting how many scoopfuls, suggest that one of them draws a tick for each scoopful whilst the other one puts the scoopful into the container. They can count the ticks once the container is full. See also Year 1 Block C Unit 2.
Extension: Decide whether to ask these children to measure in litres and 100ml increments. See also Year 2 Block C Unit 1.

BLOCK C

Activity ②

Prior learning

Children can estimate by looking and feeling. They know how to measure objects giving the measurements correctly. They can draw a picture/diagram to show how they solved the problem.

Framework objectives

● **Estimate, measure, weigh and compare objects, choosing and using suitable uniform non-standard or standard units and measuring instruments (e.g. a lever balance, metre stick or measuring jug)**
● Describe ways of solving puzzles and problems, explaining choices and decisions orally or using pictures

Vocabulary

problem, question, explain, predict, pattern, collect, organise, compare, order, sort, group, same, different, property, represent, interpret, count, tally, vote, measure, guess, length, width, height, depth, size, long, short, tall, high, low, wide, narrow, deep, shallow, thick, thin, comparatives such as longer/longest

Resources

Worksheet: Length compare
Classroom resources: metre sticks, metre tapes

② Length compare

Ask the children to work in pairs. Ask them to think of three items in the classroom that are respectively longer, taller, wider than a metre stick, and two items that are respectively shorter, narrower than the metre stick. They can measure to check their estimates. They should write their results on the worksheet 'Length compare'. Ask them to measure as accurately as they can lengths such as the height of the door, the width of the classroom and so on. They can draw a diagram to show which items are shorter, longer, or about the same length as a metre on the back of the worksheet.

Teacher support

Less confident learners: Work as a group and produce a group record of work. Encourage the children to discuss their estimates and measures, using the appropriate mathematical vocabulary.
More confident learners: Challenge these children to measure to the nearest half metre, when measuring items more than a metre long.

Common misconception

Children do not understand how to measure a longer length using a metric tape. Use a large space. Invite a child to help to pull out the tape and place it along, say, the width of the hall. Ask the rest of the class to find the beginning of the tape and to walk beside the tape, pointing to and reading aloud each metre marked on the tape. *How many metres is that in total? So how wide is the hall?* Discuss how to round up or down to the nearest metre, using vocabulary such as 'nearly', 'just over', 'under' and so on.

Probing questions

● How does your picture/diagram show what you did and what you found out?
● You found that the length of the classroom was the longest item in the room. What else did you find out about the things that you measured with the metre stick/tape?

Next steps

Support: Provide further opportunities to make estimates, and then check by measuring lengths. Include the metre stick as a standard unit. See also Year 1 Block C Unit 2.
Extension: Challenge these children to measure to the nearest 10cm using a metre stick marked in 10cm. See also Year 2 Block C Unit 1.

Activities ③ ④ and ⑤

Prior learning
Children can estimate by looking and feeling. They know how to measure objects giving the measurements correctly. They can show what they found out by using a block graph. They can sort objects in different ways. They can use what they know from comparing their lengths or balancing them.

Framework objectives
- **Estimate, measure, weigh and compare objects, choosing and using suitable uniform non-standard or standard units and measuring instruments (e.g. a lever balance, metre stick or measuring jug)**
- Use diagrams to sort objects into groups according to a given criterion; suggest a different criterion for grouping the same objects
- **Answer a question by recording information in lists and tables; present outcomes using practical resources, pictures, block graphs or pictograms**

Vocabulary
problem, question, explain, predict, pattern, collect, organise, compare, order, sort, group, same, different, property, represent, interpret, count, tally, vote, measure, weigh, guess, information, graph, block graph, pictogram, diagram, list, table, label, title, unit, centimetre (cm), metre (m), kilogram, ruler, metre stick, tape measure, balance, scales, weight, length, width, height, depth, size, long, short, tall, high, low, wide, narrow, deep, shallow, thick, thin, and comparatives such as longer/longest, heavier/heaviest

Resources
Resource sheets: Empty pictogram, Empty block graph, Self-assessment
Classroom resources: five boxes of differing lengths, widths and weights, with labels A to E (the heaviest box should not be the longest, and the shortest box should not be the lightest), items for measuring with (straws, cubes, blocks and so on), ruler marked in centimetres, two-pan balance scales

③ Sorting lengths

Ask the children to work in pairs. Ask them to decide how to sort the boxes according to length and to record their findings in a block graph or pictogram. Explain that you will ask them questions about the lengths of the boxes, so they should measure them as accurately as they can. Ask them to repeat this for the widths of the boxes. Decide whether to use the self-assessment sheet for the children to record their achievements and what they need to do next. They can attach their written work to the sheet as evidence of achievement.

Teacher support
Less confident learners: Work with these children as a group. While they work, ask how they decided to sort the boxes. Encourage them to use mathematical vocabulary correctly.
More confident learners: Provide a ruler marked in centimetres. Show the children how to measure with this to the nearest centimetre.

Common misconception
Children do not measure accurately when using non-standard uniform units.
Put a ribbon on the table. Ask children which unit they would choose to measure the length of the ribbon and why they would choose that unit. Ask them to estimate the length, and then to measure it. Check that they place the cubes, for example, end to end without leaving gaps, and that the first cube is carefully matched to one end of the ribbon. Discuss the accuracy of the measure, and whether it is nearly/just over a number or whole units, and so on.

Probing questions
- The red box was the longest object in the set. What else did you find out about it when you sorted your objects in a different way?
- Was the longest box the one that was widest? How do you know?
- What did you do to measure carefully?

BLOCK C

Next steps
Support: Provide more experience of measuring lengths with uniform non-standard units. Check that the children understand where to begin the measure, and how to deal with the approximation of nearly/just over. See also Year 1 Block C Unit 2.
Extension: Provide further experience of measuring using a ruler marked in 1cm increments. See also Year 2 Block C Unit 1.

④ Sorting weights

Ask the children to work in pairs. Ask them to decide how to sort the boxes according to weight and to record their findings in a block graph or pictogram. Explain that you will ask them questions about the weights of the boxes, so they should weigh them as accurately as they can, using the same uniform non-standard unit each time. Decide whether to use the self-assessment sheet for the children to record their achievements and what they need to do next. They can attach their written work to the sheet as evidence of achievement.

Teacher support
Less confident learners: Work with these children as a group. While the children work, ask how they decided to sort the boxes by weight. Encourage them to use mathematical vocabulary correctly.
More confident learners: Provide weights, such as 10g, 20g, 50g. The children can total the weights they use.

Common misconception
Children do not understand that, in order to make a comparison between two objects, the same uniform non-standard unit must be used.
Ask children to feel the weight of a box in their hands. Ask them to choose which unit they think would be useful for weighing the box. Ask them to count out, say, cubes onto the other pan until the pans balance. *How many cubes balanced the box?* Repeat (using a different unit) and discuss how this gave a different number for the weight. Discuss how the same unit must be used if weighing two items and comparing weights.

Probing questions
● What did you do to measure as carefully as you could?
● How do you know that the measurement is correct?
● Which was the heaviest/lightest box?
● How can you tell that from your diagram?

Next steps
Support: Provide further opportunities to compare different units for weighing items. Ask the children to make two block graphs, one showing the weights with one type of unit, and the other with the second unit. Ask them to compare the results and to note differences with the number of units involved. *Why do you think this unit gives a smaller number when we weigh with it?* See also Year 1 Block C Unit 2.
Extension: Provide further opportunities for using gram weights. Introduce the scale with a dial. See also Year 2 Block C Unit 1.

⑤ Talk about it!

Give the children a few minutes to look at their graphs from Activity 3 (Sorting lengths) and Activity 4 (Sorting weights). Ask questions such as: *Find out if the longest box is the heaviest. Are all the shorter boxes lighter than 20 cubes?* Encourage the children to discuss these two questions and to determine whether the answers are 'yes' or 'no'. Ask them to be prepared to explain their thinking. They can record their answer in a sentence on the self-assessment sheet.

Teacher support

Less confident learners: Discuss where each box is on the length and weight chart. Discuss the fact that the longest item isn't necessarily the heaviest.

More confident learners: Ask the children to explain the boxes' positions on the charts. For example, the heaviest box is beside the longest but is not the longest.

Common misconception

Children believe that because something is the longest then it must be the heaviest.

Ask children to compare some more items by length and weight. Explain that because something is the longest it may not be the heaviest, and that you cannot tell the weight of something just by looking. Repeat this for other items until children understand.

Probing questions

- Are all shorter things lighter? Why?
- Are all heavier things longer? Why?
- Is the heaviest box longest? Why?
- How can you tell from your diagrams that the heaviest box is not the longest?
- What does your block graph show about how heavy the objects are?

Next steps

Support: Provide further opportunities for comparing length and weight, and putting results into a block graph. Check that the children understand that the longest item is not necessarily the heaviest. See also Year 1 Block C Unit 2.

Extension: Ask these children to compare length, weight and capacity for several boxes and make block graphs of their results. Encourage them to describe one box in comparison to others. For example: *Box C is the longest. It is heavier than box A but not as heavy as box D. It holds more than box B but not as much as box D.* See also Year 2 Block C Unit 1.

BLOCK C

These activities can be used at the end of this block to assess those children that you think have achieved the objectives.

Recording outcomes

Objective
Answer a question by recording information in lists and tables; present outcomes using practical resources, pictures, block graphs or pictograms

Assessment focus
Level 1: Sort and classify objects, e.g. sort using one criterion or sort into disjoint sets using two simple criteria such as boy/girl or thick/thin; sort objects again using a different criterion; sort objects into a given large scale Venn or Carroll diagram. Represent their work, e.g. use the objects they have sorted as a record; use objects/pictures to create simple block graphs
Foundation stage profile scale points: Sorts or matches objects and talks about sorting. Uses developing mathematical ideas and methods to solve practical problems

Learning outcomes
- I can talk about how I solved a problem.
- I can draw pictures/diagrams to show what I have found out.
- I can show what I found out by using a block graph.

There are three parts to this activity. These can all be used together, or over several days.

1. Work with a group of 6 to 8 children. Set them a problem such as: *Here are three strips of paper. How can I tell which is longest and which is shortest?* Give the children a few minutes to discuss the problem with their partner. Ask: *How could I solve the problem?* Listen to their explanations. Invite the children to try their method and evaluate how successful they think it was. Check that they match one end of the strips of paper in order to make a good comparison. Decide whether to use the self-assessment sheet for children to record their achievements and what they need to do next. They can draw pictures to show their comparisons.
2. Ask the children to work in pairs to compare three different containers for capacity. They record their results in a diagram to show the order of capacity from least to most. Ask the children to explain how they decided to carry out the work. Decide whether to use the self-assessment sheet for the children to record their achievements and what they need to do next. They could draw pictures to show the comparison.
3. Ask the children to work in pairs to compare three parcels. Ask them to estimate the weights, then measure, using a uniform non-standard unit. They can make a block graph of their results on the resource sheet 'Empty block graph'. Ask the children to interpret their graph. For example: *Which is the heaviest parcel? How can you tell? Which is the lightest parcel? Which parcel weighs more than ___ units? Which parcel is three units heavier than ___?* The block graph can be attached to a copy of the self-assessment sheet as evidence of achievement.

Measuring

Objective
Estimate, measure, weigh and compare objects, choosing and using suitable uniform non-standard or standard units and measuring instruments (e.g. a lever balance, metre stick or measuring jug)

Learning outcomes
- I can compare the lengths/weights/capacities of more than two objects and put them in order.
- I can use equipment to measure objects.
- I can estimate by looking and feeling.
- I know how to measure objects giving the measurements correctly.

(continued on next page)

Measuring (continued)

Assessment focus

Level 1: Measure and order objects using direct comparison: compare lengths directly and put them in order; respond to and use the language of comparison: longer, longest, shorter, shortest, more, less, heavier, lighter; check which of two objects is heavier/lighter and begin to put three objects into order; find objects that are longer/shorter than a metre

Foundation stage profile scale points: Uses language such as 'greater', 'smaller', 'heavier' or 'lighter' to compare quantities

There are three parts to this activity. These can all be used together, or over several days.

1. Reveal the interactive activity 'Measuring'. Explain to the children that the items on the screen can be compared to find which is heavier or lighter. Begin by putting the pen onto one balance. *What do you think will be heavier than the pen?* Place the children's choice onto the other pan and discuss the result. Repeat this twice more. Challenge the children to order the items by weight. Let them tell you what further information they need. They can draw a diagram to show the comparisons of the weights. Provide the worksheet 'Measuring (1)'.

2. Provide the worksheet 'Measuring (2)', which is in three parts: length, weight and capacity. Ask the children to measure the items and to write their results in the data collection charts.

3. Provide the worksheet 'Measuring (3)'. This is in three parts: length, weight and capacity. Ask the children to estimate first and write their estimates, then to measure the items. Check that they make reasonable estimates.

Sorting

Objective

Use diagrams to sort objects into groups according to a given criterion; suggest a different criterion for grouping the same objects

Assessment focus

Level 1: Sort and classify objects, e.g. sort using one criterion or sort into disjoint sets using two simple criteria such as boy/girl or thick/thin; sort objects again using a different criterion; sort objects into a given large scale Venn or Carroll diagram. Represent their work, e.g. use the objects they have sorted as a record; use objects/pictures to create simple block graphs

Foundation stage profile scale points: Sorts or matches objects and talks about sorting

Learning outcomes
- I can sort objects by placing them onto a big diagram.
- I can sort objects using my own diagram to help me.
- I can sort objects in different ways. I can use what I know from comparing their lengths or balancing them.

There are three parts to this activity. These can all be used together, or over several days.

1. Use the interactive activity 'Sorting' and work with half the class at a time. Type a title (for example: Group 1's favourite food) and labels. Ask the children to look at the food icons and to choose their favourite. Invite the children, one at a time, to drag and drop their favourite food's icon into place. Ask questions about the data such as: *How many children like apples best? Which is the least favourite food? How many more like ___ than ___? How did you work that out?* Ask the children to complete the self-assessment sheet. They can write a sentence about something they can see from the pictogram.

2. Provide ribbons of different lengths. Ask the children to measure the length of the ribbons and to record their results on the resource sheet 'Empty pictogram'. Ask questions such as: *Which unit did you choose to measure the ribbons? Why did you choose that? Which ribbon is longest/shortest?* The children can attach their pictogram to the self-assessment sheet as evidence of achievement.

3. Provide four boxes. Ask the children to measure their length and weigh them, estimating first. They should put their results into a data collection table, then transfer them to the resource sheet 'Empty block graph'. *Did you make a good estimate of their lengths/weights? Which units did you choose? Why?* The children can attach their block graph to the self-assessment sheet as evidence of achievement.

Name   Date

Measuring (1)

- ◢ Choose three things in the classroom.
- ◢ Compare their lengths.
- ◢ Draw the items in the boxes to show their lengths.

Lightest   **Heaviest**

- ◢ Now choose three containers.
- ◢ Compare how much they hold.
- ◢ Draw them in these boxes.

Holds least   **Holds most**

How easy?

Red

Amber

Green

How do you think you have done?

_____

_____

Name   Date

Measuring (2)

1. Measuring lengths

◾ Choose three things to measure. Choose some units.

◾ Measure the things. Write how long each thing is in the chart.

I measured	I chose these units	How long

2. Measuring weight

◾ Choose three things to weigh. Choose some units.

◾ Weigh the things. Write how heavy each thing is in the chart.

I measured	I chose these units	How heavy

3. Measuring capacity

◾ Choose three containers. Choose some units.

◾ Measure how much the containers hold. Write how much each container holds in the chart.

I measured	I chose these units	How much it holds

How easy?

Red
Amber
Green

How do you think you have done?

_____

_____

Name	Date

Measuring (3)

- ◾ Choose four boxes to measure.
- ◾ Estimate their length.
- ◾ Write this in the chart.
- ◾ Now measure the boxes.

I chose	My estimate	My measure

- ◾ Do this again for the weight of the boxes.

I chose	My estimate	My measure

- ◾ Now do this again for how much the boxes hold.

I chose	My estimate	My measure

Answer these questions:

1. Which box is the longest?

2. Is the box that is longest the same as the one that holds the most?

3. Is the box that is lightest the same as the box which holds least?

How easy?

Red
Amber
Green

How do you think you have done?

_____

_____

BLOCK D
Calculating, measuring and understanding shape

Expected prior learning
Check that children can already:
- use language such as 'more' or 'less' to compare two numbers
- relate addition to combining two groups of objects and subtraction to 'taking away'
- use some of the vocabulary involved in adding and subtracting
- use everyday words to describe position
- use language such as 'greater', 'smaller', 'heavier' or 'lighter' to compare quantities
- use everyday language related to time and sequence familiar events.

Objectives overview
The text in this diagram identifies the focus of mathematics learning within the block.

Key aspects of learning
- Problem solving
- Information processing
- Communication

Solving problems involving counting, adding, subtracting, doubling or halving numbers, money, measures or time

Estimating, measuring, weighing and comparing objects, using uniform non-standard or standard units

Time to the hour and half hour

Days of the week and months of the year

BLOCK D: Calculating, measuring and understanding shape

Counting on

Finding a difference

Adding or subtracting a one-digit number or multiple of 10 to/from a two-digit number

Position, direction and movement

Everyday language

Unit 1 ◻ Calculating, measuring and understanding shape

Introduction

In this unit, children should be encouraged to talk about their day, ordering events. They should listen to stories during the day, not necessarily during their mathematics time, such as *The Very Hungry Caterpillar* or *The Bad-tempered Ladybird* by Eric Carle, and retell the story, ordering the events. All of the work in the unit is about solving problems, so children should be encouraged to discuss with their partner or within their group how to set about the task. They continue to practise counting objects, and the contexts here are money and measures. They extend their understanding of time, as well as using the vocabulary of position and movement in context.

BLOCK D

Framework objectives	Assessment focuses		Success criteria for Year 1	Learning outcomes
	Foundation stage profile scale point	Level 1		
① Measure it ② Weigh it				
Estimate, measure, weigh and compare objects, choosing and using suitable uniform non-standard or standard units and measuring instruments (e.g. a lever balance, metre stick or measuring jug)	SSM 7 Uses language such as 'greater', 'smaller', 'heavier' or 'lighter' to compare quantities	• measure and order objects using direct comparison	• makes a reasonable estimate of length, weight and capacity using appropriate units, then checks by measuring • can read whether something is about the same weight, heavier or lighter than the units, by observing the position of the pans on the balance • for length, lines up one end of the item with the first non-standard uniform unit • either counts and remembers how many units, or makes a chart to keep track, when finding capacity using non-standard uniform units	*I can guess how many cubes will balance a parcel. I can use a metre stick to measure how far it is across the hall.*
③ Count the paces				
Solve problems involving counting, adding, subtracting, doubling or halving in the context of numbers, measures or money, for example to 'pay' and 'give change'	NLC 8 Uses developing mathematical ideas and methods to solve practical problems	• use mathematics as an integral part of classroom activities, e.g. with support • engage with practical mathematical activities involving sorting, counting and measuring by direct comparison • begin to understand the relevance of mathematical ideas to everyday situations by using them in role-play	• can count non-standard uniform units of length, weight and capacity accurately • understands that the last number said in a count represents how many • can use counting to solve a problem such as comparing two items for length, weight or capacity	*I can use counting to solve problems involving measures.*

Unit 1 📖 Calculating, measuring and understanding shape

Framework objectives	Assessment focuses		Success criteria for Year 1	Learning outcomes
	Foundation stage profile scale point	Level 1		
Count reliably at least 20 objects, recognising that when rearranged the number of objects stays the same; estimate a number of objects that can be checked by counting	NLC 6 Counts reliably up to 10 everyday objects	• count up to 10 objects	• can count how many using a strategy such as touch/point, say the number name and move the item • recognises that the last number in a count represents how many there are • can count things that cannot be seen, such as paces across a room, accurately, and knows that the last number said represents how many there are	I can find out how long a room is by counting the paces I take to cross it.

④ Where is it?

| Visualise and use everyday language to describe the position of objects and direction and distance when moving them, for example when placing or moving objects on a game board | SSM 5 Uses everyday words to describe position | • use everyday language to describe positions of 2D and 3D shapes
• respond to and use positional language, e.g. 'behind', 'under', 'on top of', 'next to', 'in between'... | • can use the vocabulary of position and movement to describe where something is
• can follow instructions for position and movement accurately | I can describe where something is using words like 'next to', 'in front of', 'underneath', 'on top of'... |

⑤ Days of the week ⑥ Humpty Dumpty in order

| Use vocabulary related to time; order days of the week and months; read the time to the hour and half hour | There is no assessment focus for this level | • order events
• order everyday events and describe the sequence
• use the vocabulary of time including days of the week | • can use the vocabulary of time appropriately
• knows the days of the week, says them in order, and knows the position of the days relative to other days
• can tell a story in order | I know the days of the week and can say them in order.
I can remember the order of a favourite story. |

Activities and

Prior learning
Children can use counting to solve problems involving measures. They can guess how many cubes will balance a parcel. They can use a metre stick to measure how far it is across the hall.

Framework objective
Estimate, measure, weigh and compare objects, choosing and using suitable uniform non-standard or standard units and measuring instruments (e.g. a lever balance, metre stick or measuring jug)

Vocabulary
problem, method, number sentence, explain, record, compare, order, measure, weigh, long, longer, longest, short, shorter, shortest, tall, taller, tallest, light, lighter, lightest, heavy, heavier, heaviest, hold more, holds less, ruler, tape measure, metre stick, balance, scales, measuring jug

Resources
Resource sheet: Self-assessment
Classroom resources: cubes, items to be weighed that can be weighed with up to 20 cubes, metre sticks, two-pan balance scales

① Measure it

This activity is best carried out with a group of about eight children, working in pairs. Ask them to use a metre stick to measure the width of the hall. Observe how they go about the task, how they keep count of the number of metres, and how they match the metre stick end to the previous end of the metre stick on the floor. Once they have completed this activity, decide whether to use the self-assessment sheet for the children to record their achievements and what they need to do next. They can record the width of the hall in metres on the self-assessment sheet.

Teacher support
Less confident learners: Check that the children can use the metre stick appropriately, placing one end at the end-point of the previous metre stick on the floor.
More confident learners: Challenge these children to measure the length of the hall in metres. Check how they keep count of the number of metres.

Common misconceptions
When measuring with a metre stick, children do not understand that the metre stick must be laid at the end of the previous metre.
Demonstrate how to measure using a metre stick. If children need a visual clue as to where the metre stick was, make a chalk mark, and butt the metre stick up to the mark.

Children do not keep an accurate count of the number of metres.
Suggest that children write a number on paper: 1, 2, 3 (and so on) for each metre measured. Check that they understand that the last number written is the number of metres measured.

Probing questions
● Which two lengths are the same? Now find a length that is longer than this.
● Where do you start to measure the length of the carpet?
● Ann measured the height of these two dolls in blocks. How many blocks taller is the large doll?

Next steps
Support: Provide further opportunities for the children to measure with a metre stick and keep count of the number of metres, such as measuring the width and length of the classroom. See also Foundation Stage Overview of Learning 13.
Extension: Provide opportunities for the children to measure longer lengths, using a metre tape. See also Year 1 Block C Unit 2.

② Weigh it

Let the children each hold in their hands the first item to be weighed. They should also try holding some cubes for comparison. *How many cubes do you think this item weighs?* Ask a child to weigh the item. Check that the child recognises when balance has been achieved. *Did you make a good guess?* Repeat for other items until each child has weighed one of the items. Check that the children's estimates are reasonable. Decide whether to use the self-assessment sheet for the children to record their achievements and what they need to do next. They can record their estimates and the weight of each item on the back of the sheet.

Teacher support
Less confident learners: Choose items that weigh up to six cubes.
More confident learners: Challenge these children to estimate and weigh an item using cubes, and then with another unit, such as cups of sand. Ask them to explain why the measurements do not have the same numbers.

Common misconception
Children do not make reasonable estimates of weight.
Ask children to hold an item to be weighed, and then to hold the units to be used, such as cubes. Now ask them to give an estimate of how much the item weighs. Check this by weighing using a two-pan balance. Repeat for another item, and check that children's estimates are becoming more reasonable.

Probing questions
● How did you find out which of these two objects was the lighter/shorter/held the least amount?
● Did you make a good estimate of weight? Was it close to the measurement?

Next steps
Support: Repeat the activity over time, extending the counting range by using heavier objects, until the children can count out at least 20 units. See also Foundation Stage Overview of Learning 13.
Extension: Challenge the children to estimate and weigh some items, choosing their own uniform non-standard units. Ask them to explain their choice of units and whether or not they thought these were appropriate. See also Year 1 Blocks C and D Units 2.

Activity ③

Prior learning
Children can use counting to solve problems involving measures. They can find out how long a room is by counting the paces they take to cross it.

Framework objectives
● Solve problems involving counting, adding, subtracting, doubling or halving in the context of numbers, measures or money, for example to 'pay' and 'give change'
● Count reliably at least 20 objects, recognising that when rearranged the number of objects stays the same; estimate a number of objects that can be checked by counting

Vocabulary
problem, method, number sentence, explain, record, compare, order, measure, weigh, count, guess, estimate, roughly, enough, not enough, too much, too little, too many, too few, more, less, the same number as, equals (=)

Resources
Resource sheet: Self-assessment
Classroom resources: two PE cones

③ Count the paces

This activity is suitable for a group of six to eight children. Ask the children to estimate how many paces they would need to take to cross the room. Ask them, one at a time, to cross the room, taking normal-sized paces. They count each pace aloud. Encourage the other children to count the paces, doing so either silently (if they can) or very quietly. *How many paces were there? Did you all count the same number?* Decide whether to use the self-assessment sheet for the children to record their achievements and what they need to do next. They can write their estimate and count of their steps on the sheet.

Teacher support
Less confident learners: Put out two PE cones about three or four metres apart. Children stand by one cone, estimate the number of paces, and check by walking.
More confident learners: Decide whether to increase the distance to a count of more than 20. Discuss the children's strategies for keeping count.

Common misconception
Children do not synchronise the step and count so that the count is inaccurate. Ask children to count their steps with you. Use a strong voice where necessary to keep the count in time with the step. Repeat this several times until the child is confident with counting steps. For counts to 10, some children may find it helpful to say the number and keep a tally on their fingers.

Probing questions
● Guess how many cubes are in the jar. Now check by counting. Why did you think it was that number of cubes?
● How many paces did you estimate for crossing the room? What did you count? Did you make a good estimate?

Next steps
Support: Provide further opportunities for counting movements, keeping the number below 10 at first. See also Foundation Stage Overview of Learning 3.
Extension: Challenge the children to count larger numbers of movements. Ask them to compare results for two children walking the same distance, and to explain why the numbers are not the same. See also Year 1 Block A Unit 2.

BLOCK D

Activity ④

Prior learning
Children can describe where something is using words like 'next to', 'in front of', 'underneath', 'on top of' and so on.

Framework objective
Visualise and use everyday language to describe the position of objects and direction and distance when moving them, for example when placing or moving objects on a game board

Vocabulary
position, direction, grid, outside, inside, beside, next to, front, back, between, centre, underneath, above, on top of, below, half way, near, far, whole turn, half turn, quarter turn, right, left

Resources
Worksheet: Where is it?

④ Where is it?

This activity is most suited to a group of four to six children working with a teacher or learning support assistant. Provide copies of the worksheet 'Where is it'?. Ask questions about the position of the animals, such as: *Point to the monkey. Point to another monkey. Which monkey is higher/lower? Which animal is in the water?* Now ask the children to answer in a sentence, using the appropriate vocabulary: *Where is the lion? Where is the seal? Which animal is behind the penguin?* Check that the children understand and can use the vocabulary of position.

Teacher support
Less confident learners: Use an enlarged A3 copy of the worksheet 'Where is it?' as well as each child having their own copy. At first, give instructions: *Point to...*
More confident learners: Ask these children to choose any animal and describe its position in relation to another animal.

Common misconception
Children do not understand the vocabulary of position.
Ask children to follow your instructions: *Stand in front of/behind/opposite/ between... Show me your right hand. Tell me something higher/lower than...* Repeat this frequently until children know and can use this vocabulary.

Probing questions
● Stand in front of/behind/beside/opposite a partner. Stand between two other children.
● Tell me something in the classroom that is higher than/lower than/above/ below/between/beside/next to/in the middle of/at the edge of/in the corner of...

Next steps
Support: Provide further opportunities for following instructions and for explaining where something is (for example, during PE lessons and in oral and mental starters). See also Foundation Stage Overview of Learning 12.
Extension: Play 'Simon says' with the children. Invite them to suggest some of the things that Simon could say, using the appropriate vocabulary. See also Year 1 Block D Unit 2.

BLOCK D

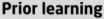

Activities ⑤ and ⑥

Prior learning
Children know the days of the week and can say them in order. They can remember the order of a favourite story.

Framework objective
Use vocabulary related to time; order days of the week and months; read the time to the hour and half hour

Vocabulary
time, clock, hands, morning, afternoon, evening, midnight, hour, night, day, week, days of the week

Resources
Interactive activity: Humpty Dumpty in order
Worksheets: Days of the week (A3 and copied onto card), Humpty Dumpty in order (1) and (2)
Resource sheet: Self-assessment
Classroom resources: glue, scissors

⑤ Days of the week

Ask the children to say the days of the week in order. Note who is confident with this and who needs more support. Ask questions about the days of the week, such as: *What day is it today? So what will it be tomorrow? What day was it yesterday? Which days do we come to school? Which days do we stay at home? Which day do you like best? Why is that?* Decide whether to use the self-assessment sheet for the children to record their achievements and what they need to do next. They can write the days of the week in order on the sheet.

Teacher support
Less confident learners: Put the cards from the worksheet 'Days of the week' in order. Say the days together, pointing to each day as it is spoken.
More confident learners: Ask these children to list the days and to draw a picture for each to show what is special for them about that day.

Common misconception
Children do not remember the order of the days of the week.
Say rhymes and sing songs that feature the days of the week in order. Repeat this often until children can say the days in order without prompting.

Probing questions
● What day is it today? So what will tomorrow be?
● Which are the weekend days?
● Which days are we at school?

Next steps
Support: Continue to say together the days of the week in order, perhaps as part of an oral and mental starter. Ask questions about the days, such as: *Which day comes after/before ___?* See also Foundation Stage Overview of Learning 14.
Extension: Invite the children to take turns to write that day's name on the board. Challenge them to learn the month names, in order, and to begin to write the month as well. See also Year 1 Block D Unit 2.

BLOCK D

⑥ Humpty Dumpty in order

Provide each child with a copy of the worksheet 'Humpty Dumpty in order (1)', and scissors. Explain that the pictures are muddled up. Ask the children to cut their pictures apart and to put them in story order. Allow a few minutes for this to be done. Now reveal the interactive activity 'Humpty Dumpty in order'. Ask the children to explain where each picture on the screen goes in order to match the words of the rhyme provided on the left-hand side of the screen. Invite children to come to the whiteboard to drag and drop the pictures into the right order. The children can glue their pictures in order onto the worksheet 'Humpty Dumpty in order (2)'.

Teacher support
Less confident learners: Work with these children as a group to decide on the order of the pictures.
More confident learners: Ask the children to think of another favourite rhyme and to draw their own pictures to tell the story in the correct order.

Common misconception
Children do not tell a story in order.
Provide opportunities for children to listen to a story, or learn a new rhyme. Ask them to tell the story in order. Repeat this for events in their lives, so that children order events in the school day, or, for example, what they did at home at the weekend. Repeat this until they can confidently retell a story or event, in order.

Probing questions
● Look at these pictures. Point to a picture that shows something that you think happened first.
● Point to a picture that shows something that you think happened second.
● Point to a picture that shows something that you think happened last.

Next steps
Support: Provide further opportunities for the children to retell a story, or to discuss a special event, and to order what happens. See also Foundation Stage Overview of Learning 14.
Extension: Challenge the children to retell more complex events or stories, sequencing these correctly. See also Year 1 Block D Unit 2.

BLOCK D

Unit 2 ▢ Calculating, measuring and understanding shape

Introduction
In this unit, children work in pairs or groups and use the vocabulary of the mathematics topic in order to plan their work and to carry it out. They solve problems for time, position, direction and turn, measures and money. For money problems they use their addition and subtraction skills to work out how much money to give and how much change they will receive. Throughout the unit children should be encouraged to record their work, using number sentences where appropriate.

Framework objectives	Assessment focuses		Success criteria for Year 1	Learning outcomes
	Foundation stage profile scale point	Level 1		
① Weighing ② Filling and pouring				
Solve problems involving counting, adding, subtracting, doubling or halving in the context of numbers, measures or money, for example to 'pay' and 'give change'	NLC 8 Uses developing mathematical ideas and methods to solve practical problems	• solve addition/subtraction problems involving up to 10 objects, e.g. • given a number work out 'how many more to make…' • choose which of given pairs of numbers add to a given total • solve measuring problems such as how many balance with…	• can use addition and subtraction to solve measuring problems	*I can add up and take away when I measure.*
Estimate, measure, weigh and compare objects, choosing and using suitable uniform non-standard or standard units and measuring instruments (e.g. a lever balance, metre stick or measuring jug)	SSM 7 Uses language such as 'greater', 'smaller', 'heavier' or 'lighter' to compare quantities	• measure and order objects using direct comparison • draw simple conclusions from their work, e.g. with support • identify which set has most, which object is biggest, smallest, tallest, etc	• can estimate capacity using non-standard uniform units by looking • can check the estimate by filling and pouring • can estimate weights by lifting and feeling both the parcel and the chosen non-standard uniform units • can check the estimate by weighing	*I can guess how many jugs of water I will put into the bowl to fill it. I can use the red weights to balance a parcel.*
③ Shopping totals ④ Shopping change				
Relate addition to counting on; recognise that addition can be done in any order; use practical and informal written methods to support the addition of a one-digit number or a multiple of 10 to a one-digit or two-digit number	C 4 Relates addition by combining two groups	• solve addition/subtraction problems involving up to 10 objects, e.g. • solve problems involving 1p or £1 coins	• can use counting on to add or subtract • knows that addition can be done in any order • can find prices using addition, counting on from the larger number	*I can buy two toys and work out how much they cost altogether.*

Unit 2 ▢ Calculating, measuring and understanding shape

Framework objectives	Assessment focuses		Success criteria for Year 1	Learning outcomes
	Foundation stage profile scale point	Level 1		
Understand subtraction as 'take away' and find a 'difference' by counting up; use practical and informal written methods to support the subtraction of a one-digit number from a one-digit or two-digit number and a multiple of 10 from a two-digit number	C 5 Relates subtraction to taking away	● add and subtract numbers of objects to 10 ● draw simple conclusions from their work, e.g. with support ● explain numbers and calculations, how many altogether, how many used or hidden, how many left, how many each, etc	● can use counting up to find a difference ● can find change from 20p by counting up from the cost number	I can work out how much I have left from 20p when I buy a toy.

⑤ Make a shape

Visualise and use everyday language to describe the position of objects and direction and distance when moving them, for example when placing or moving objects on a game board	SSM 5 Uses everyday words to describe position	● use everyday language to describe positions of 2D and 3D shapes ● respond to and use positional language, e.g. 'behind', 'under', 'on top of', 'next to', 'in between'...	● can use the vocabulary appropriately to describe the position of objects ● can give instructions using appropriate vocabulary of position ● can follow instructions to make a shape	I can tell my partner where to place their cubes to make the same shape as mine. I can follow instructions to make the same shape as my partner.

⑥ Clock

Use vocabulary related to time; order days of the week and months; read the time to the hour and half hour	There is no assessment focus for this level	● order events ● read the time on an analogue clock at the hour and begin to know the half hour	● can use the vocabulary of time appropriately ● knows the order of the days of the week and months ● recognises o'clock time and can explain where the hands will point for a given o'clock time	I know that it is 3 o'clock when the big hand points to the 12 and the small hand points to the 3.

⑦ Turning yourself

Identify objects that turn about a point (e.g. scissors) or about a line (e.g. a door); recognise and make whole, half and quarter turns	SSM 5 Uses everyday words to describe position	● use everyday language to describe positions of 2D and 3D shapes ● respond to and use directional language in talk about objects and movement, e.g. 'forwards', 'backwards', 'turn'	● responds appropriately to the vocabulary of turning ● recognises whole, half and quarter turns and can follow instructions to make these turns	I know how to turn right and to turn left.

BLOCK D

Activities ① and ②

Prior learning
Children can add up and take away when they measure. They can guess how many jugs of water they will put into the bowl to fill it. They can use the red weights to balance a parcel.

Framework objectives
● Solve problems involving counting, adding, subtracting, doubling or halving in the context of numbers, measures or money, for example to 'pay' and 'give change'
● **Estimate, measure, weigh and compare objects, choosing and using suitable uniform non-standard or standard units and measuring instruments (e.g. a lever balance, metre stick or measuring jug)**

Vocabulary
lightest, heavy, heavier, heaviest, hold more, holds less, balance, scales, measuring jug, problem, method, number sentence, explain, record, compare, order, measure, weigh

Resources
Worksheet: Filling and pouring
Resource sheet: Self-assessment
Classroom resources: non-standard uniform units for weighing (such as cubes), three parcels, two-pan balance, three containers of different capacities, cup (as the uniform non-standard unit), water or sand for filling and pouring

① Weighing

Ask the children to work in pairs. Say: *Look at these three parcels. Find out how much each weighs. Estimate first.* Ask them to decide how to record their estimates and results. Give them ten minutes to complete this task. Now explain that you will ask them to write some number sentences for you about their parcels (such as 6 − 3 = 3) and say what this means in words: *Parcel A is three cubes lighter than parcel B. Which is the lightest/heaviest parcel? How much more does the heaviest parcel weigh than the lightest? Write a number sentence.* Decide whether to use the self-assessment sheet for the children to record their achievements and what they need to do next.

Teacher support
Less confident learners: Work together as a group to carry out the activity and to write the number sentences.
More confident learners: Provide another parcel and ask the children to write more number sentences to show the comparisons of weight.

Common misconception
Children do not measure weight accurately.
Provide a two-pan balance, a parcel and some cubes. Ask children to estimate how much they think the parcel weighs. Ask them to check by weighing and observe their technique. Discuss how sometimes one more cube is too many, and yet removing that cube from the balance does not balance the parcel 'perfectly'. Explain that when weighing children should choose the nearest number of cubes to make a good balance. Repeat for other parcels. Use the vocabulary of approximation to describe the weight of a parcel, such as 'nearly', 'just over' and so on.

Probing questions
● Which of these packages is the heaviest? How do you know? How could you check?
● Is the red parcel heavier than this? How do you know?
● How much heavier/lighter is it? How did you work that out?
● Would it be fair to measure with ___? Why/why not?

■ SCHOLASTIC

Next steps

Support: Provide further opportunities for estimating and weighing. Ask the children to compare the weights of two parcels to find the difference, and to find totals of their weight. See also Year 1 Block D Unit 1 and Block C Unit 2.

Extension: Challenge the children to compare the weights of four parcels, then to find the answers to questions such as: *What is the difference in weight between these two parcels? What is the total weight of the parcels?* Ask the children to write number sentences to demonstrate their answers. See also Year 1 Block C Unit 3.

② Filling and pouring

Ask the children to work in pairs. Explain that you would like them to estimate and then measure the capacity of three containers, using a cup as a non-standard uniform unit. Ask them to record their results, including their estimates. Encourage them to write number sentences to show the difference in capacity between two of the containers (such as 5 − 3 = 2), and then their total (such as 3 + 5 = 8). The worksheet 'Filling and pouring' has a data collection table to help children count how many cupfuls each container makes.

Teacher support

Less confident learners: Work as a group to complete the task, including finding differences and totals of capacities.

More confident learners: Provide another container and challenge the children to find the totals of three, then four, containers' capacities.

Common misconception

Children do not make accurate checks of capacity.

Observe children measuring the capacity of a container. Discuss how they need to keep a check of how many cupfuls they have poured into the container. They might make a mark on paper for each cupful. Discuss how it is important to keep a count of how many units they have used. Repeat this for another container and check that children do now keep a paper record for each unit they use.

Probing questions

- Which of these containers holds the most water? How do you know? How could you check?
- Did you make a good estimate? How do you know?
- Which of these objects are sensible to use for measuring? Why?
- Would it be fair to measure with ___? Why/why not?

Next steps

Support: Provide further opportunities for estimating and measuring capacity. Encourage the children to keep a paper and pencil check of how many units they need to fill a container. Ask them to find the differences and totals of capacity between two small containers. See also Year 1 Block C Unit 2 and Block D Unit 1.

Extension: Challenge the children to estimate, then measure, the capacities of four containers. Ask them to order the containers by capacity and find the differences between each pair of containers in their order. See also Year 1 Block C Unit 3.

Activities ③ and ④

Prior learning
Children can buy two toys and work out how much they cost altogether. They can work out how much they have left from 20p when they buy a toy.

Framework objectives
● Relate addition to counting on; recognise that addition can be done in any order; use practical and informal written methods to support the addition of a one-digit number or a multiple of 10 to a one-digit or two-digit number
● Understand subtraction as 'take away' and find a 'difference' by counting up; use practical and informal written methods to support the subtraction of a one-digit number from a one-digit or two-digit number and a multiple of 10 from a two-digit number

Vocabulary
count, the same number as, equals, add, plus, sum, total, altogether, subtract, minus, take away, difference, double, halve, half, quarter, how many?, how much? money, coin, pence, penny, pound, pay, change, buy, sell, price, spend

Resources
Interactive activities: Shopping totals, Shopping change
Classroom resources: 1p, 2p, 5p, 10p coins; class shop with items to buy up to 20p

③ Shopping totals

This activity is best done with a group of six to eight children. Reveal the interactive activity 'Shopping totals'. Drag and drop the car and the ball into the shopping basket. Ask: *What is the total of 6p and 4p?* Ask the children to suggest which coins could be used to make the total. Invite a child to come to the board to drag the suggested coins onto the tray and then enter the total amount into the blank space to complete the number sentence. Invite the children to explain how they calculated the answer. Repeat for other pairs of toys, keeping the totals to up to 20p.

Teacher support
Less confident learners: Provide coins for the children to use to find the totals.
More confident learners: Ask these children to say which coins could be used to make the total, using the least number of coins each time.

Common misconception
Children do not have suitable strategies for totalling two prices.
Ask: *What is 6p and 3p? How can we work this out?* Discuss how one way is to begin with the larger number and count on for the smaller number. Say: *6 and 7, 8, 9. So 6p and 3p is 9p.* Suggest that children keep a tally of how many they have counted on using their fingers. Repeat for other amounts with totals up to 10p.

Probing questions
● How did you work out how much these two items cost altogether?
● Does it cost more if I buy them in a different order?
● Make up a question using the words 'sum of' and tell me how to do it.
● Tell me some addition questions that have 20p as an answer.

Next steps
Support: Provide a class shop where the children can practise buying two items. Provide coins that can be used as a counting aid. See also Year 1 Block A Unit 2.
Extension: Challenge the children to buy three things from the class shop and total the prices. Ask them to find the total and change from 20p. See also Year 1 Block A Unit 3.

BLOCK D

④ Shopping change

Reveal the interactive activity 'Shopping change'. Look at the first screen, which shows a toy car priced at 6p. Ask: *How much change would there be from 20p?* Ask the children to work out the answer, and then invite a volunteer to come to the board to drag and drop the right amount of coins onto the tray. Check that the children count up. As they drop the coins onto the tray the amount is automatically calculated in the number sentence.Check that the children use appropriate coins, and do not count up using just 1p coins. Repeat the activity on the subsequent screens.

Teacher support
Less confident learners: Use prices up to 10p and change from 10p.
More confident learners: Challenge the children to work mentally, counting up in their heads. Check that they can find the least number of coins to make the change.

Common misconception
Children do not understand the value of coins.
Children may count all coins as '1p'. Ask them to find equivalent values for coins. Begin with the 2p coin: two 1p coins. Ask them to find equivalent values for the 5p coin, such as 2p, 2p, 1p, or five 1p coins, and so on. Repeat this for the 10p coin, then when children understand about equivalent values the 20p coin. Now ask them to find change from 5p for a spend of 3p. Ask them to use the least number of coins. Repeat for other values and extend to 10p over time.

Probing questions
● How did you work out how much you had left?
● Make up a 'take away' question and show me how to do it.
● Tell me some subtraction questions that have 10p as an answer.

Next steps
Support: Provide further opportunities for buying in the class shop and receiving change. The children should, over time, take the role of both shopkeeper and customer. Check that they use appropriate coins for giving change, that they count up from the price, and that over time they use the least number of coins. See also Year 1 Block A Unit 2.
Extension: Ask the children to buy two items in the class shop, total their cost and calculate the change from 20p. They should, over time, take the role of both shopkeeper and customer. See also Year 1 Block A Unit 3.

Activity ⑤

Prior learning
Children can tell their partner where to place their cubes to make the same shape as theirs. They can follow instructions to make the same shape as their partner.

Framework objective
Visualise and use everyday language to describe the position of objects and direction and distance when moving them, for example when placing or moving objects on a game board

Vocabulary
position, direction, grid, outside, inside, beside, next to, front, back, between, centre, underneath, above, on top of, below, half way, near, far, whole turn, half turn, quarter turn, right, left

Resources
Resource sheet: Self-assessment
Classroom resources: interlocking cubes, large book to make a screen between two children

⑤ Make a shape

Ask the children to work in pairs with some interlocking cubes, and to place a large book between them to make a screen. One of them makes a shape with the cubes, without their partner seeing it. Now they give instructions for their partner to make the shape. When they have finished, they compare their shapes to check that they are the same. They repeat this, with the other child making the shape, hidden from their partner. Decide whether to use the self-assessment sheet for the children to record their achievements and what they need to do next. They can sketch one of their shapes on the sheet.

Teacher support
Less confident learners: Work as a group. Check that the children understand and follow instructions and that they can use the appropriate vocabulary when it is their turn to give instructions.
More confident learners: Challenge these children to make a more complex shape for their partner to make.

Common misconception
Children do not understand the vocabulary of position.
Work in a large space. Ask children to follow the instructions that you give. Say, for example: *Find a partner. One of you stand in front of your partner. Who is in front? Who is behind? Now one of you move to the right and the other to the left of the room. Who has moved to the right/left?* Now ask the children to work in threes. One of them gives instructions for the other two to follow. Check that they use the vocabulary appropriately and that the others understand the instructions.

Probing questions
● Look at my shape. Where is the red cube? Shut your eyes. [Change the shape.] Now where is my red cube?
● Put the red cube on the table. Put the blue cube on top of the red. Put the yellow cube between the red and the blue.

Next steps
Support: Provide further opportunities for following instructions for position and movement, such as during a PE lesson, where children move themselves following instructions. See also Year 1 Block D Unit 1.
Extension: Ask the children to play 'Simon says' with the other children. They give instructions for moving arms and hands. See also Year 1 Block D Unit 3.

BLOCK D

Activity ⑥

Prior learning
Children know that it is 3 o'clock when the big hand points to the 12 and the small hand points to the 3.

Framework objective
Use vocabulary related to time; order days of the week and months; read the time to the hour and half hour

Vocabulary
time, clock, hands, morning, afternoon, evening, midnight, hour, night, day, week, year, days of the week, o'clock

Resources
Resource sheets: Clock face, Self-assessment
Classroom resources: teaching clock, clock stamp and ink

⑥ Clock

Photocopy several copies of the resource sheet 'Clock face' onto A4 card, cut out the hands and use paper fasteners to pin them to the clock face so that each child has one. Ask the children to listen carefully to the time that you say. They set the hands on their clock faces to this o'clock time, and, when you say *Show me*, they hold up their clock faces for you to see. Show each time on the teaching clock so that the children can check their own clock face. In pairs, the children take turns to say o'clock times for their partners to show on their clock face. Decide whether to use the self-assessment sheet for the children to record their achievements and what they need to do next. They can stamp some clock faces onto the sheet and draw in the hands to show some o'clock times.

Teacher support
Less confident learners: Work as a group. At first show the teaching clock. Discuss where each hand is for o'clock times that the children say. Say different times, and ask the children to show these on their own clock faces.
More confident learners: Include half-past times.

Common misconception
Children do not differentiate between the hands of the clock.
Compare the lengths of the two hands and check that children see that one is longer than the other. Discuss how the little hand tells us which hour it is and that when the big hand is on 12 then it is an o'clock time. Demonstrate this on the teaching clock. Turn the hands slowly to the next hour so that children can see how the hands move. Repeat this until children are confident.

Probing questions
● Turn the hands of this clock so that it shows 4 o'clock.
● Who took the shortest time to...?
● What does the big hand tell us?
● What does the small hand tell us?

Next steps
Support: Provide further opportunities for telling the o'clock time. See also Year 1 Block D Unit 1.
Extension: Encourage the children to tell the time to the half hour. Ask them to discuss the position of both of the clock hands at the half hour. See also Year 1 Block D Unit 3.

BLOCK D

Activity ⑦

Prior learning
Children know how to turn right and to turn left.

Framework objective
Identify objects that turn about a point (e.g. scissors) or about a line (e.g. a door); recognise and make whole, half and quarter turns

Vocabulary
position, direction, grid, outside, inside, beside, next to, front, back, between, centre, underneath, above, on top of, below, half way, near, far, whole turn, half turn, quarter turn, right, left

Resources
Resource sheet: Self-assessment
Classroom resources: large space for children to move in

⑦ Turning yourself

Work in a large space. Ask the children to follow instructions for turning. Say, for example: *Move forwards/backwards. Turn left/right. Move in a straight line. Now turn right and take three steps forwards.* Check that they understand the instructions and can make appropriate turns left and right. Decide whether to use the self-assessment sheet for the children to record their achievements and what they need to do next. They can write a sentence about turning left and right on the sheet.

Teacher support
Less confident learners: If the children find the activity difficult, ask them to line up behind you. Say the instructions, move slowly and ask the children to follow your instructions and movements.
More confident learners: Include more complex movements, such as: *Turn right, move forward three paces, then turn left.*

Common misconception
Children do not differentiate between left and right.
Provide some arm bands and ask children to put the band onto their right arm. When you ask them to turn right they turn their body towards their right arm. The other arm is their left arm, and when they are asked to turn to the left they turn towards the arm without the armband on. Repeat the activity above. Check that children now recognise right and left. Repeat several times over the course of a few days in order that they feel confident with which is left and which is right.

Probing questions
● Which of these shapes will roll in a straight line? Which will roll in a curved line?
● Follow my instructions to get through the maze. Move forwards, turn left, go straight on, turn the corner.

Next steps
Support: Include turning left and right regularly as part of PE. Check that the children do recognise which is which and turn accordingly. See also Year 1 Block D Unit 1.
Extension: Encourage the children to move a programmable toy through a maze and to include turning left and right. See also Year 1 Block D Unit 3.

BLOCK D

Unit 3 ▦ Calculating, measuring and understanding shape

Introduction

In this unit, children develop their ability to explain their work and how they carried it out. They record using pictures, diagrams or number sentences and explain why they made their choices. Children are engaged in solving problems, using their counting and addition and subtraction skills. They develop their understanding of money, paying and giving change, and respond to money word problems. They learn about the months of the year, make a class calendar, and tell the time to o'clock and half past. They estimate, measure and compare units to find the most suitable. They develop their understanding of position, direction and movement, including understanding that some things turn on the spot and some turn on a line.

Framework objectives	Assessment focuses		Success criteria for Year 1	Learning outcomes
	Foundation stage profile scale point	Level 1		
① Using coins ② Half price ⑤ Measure the box				
Solve problems involving counting, adding, subtracting, doubling or halving in the context of numbers, measures or money, for example to 'pay' and 'give change'	NLC 8 Uses developing mathematical ideas and methods to solve practical problems	• solve addition/subtraction problems involving up to 10 objects, e.g. ● solve measuring problems such as how many balance with... ● solve problems involving 1p or £1 coins	• can make comparisons of three objects by using the scales • can order the objects by weight • can pay for something, giving coins to the value of the exact price • can work out half of a price	*I can find out which of three objects is the heaviest by using the scales.* *I can work out which coins to use to pay the exact price for something.* *I can work out what something costs when it is half price.*
① Using coins ② Half price				
Relate addition to counting on; recognise that addition can be done in any order; use practical and informal written methods to support the addition of a one-digit number or a multiple of 10 to a one-digit or two-digit number	C 4 Relates addition by combining two groups	• solve addition/subtraction problems involving up to 10 objects, e.g. ● solve problems involving 1p or £1 coins	• can count in 10s to solve a problem • can use counting on from the larger number to add	*I can work out how many 10p badges I can buy for £1.*

Unit 3 ◻ Calculating, measuring and understanding shape

Framework objectives	Assessment focuses		Success criteria for Year 1	Learning outcomes
	Foundation stage profile scale point	Level 1		
③ Giving change				
Understand subtraction as 'take away' and find a 'difference' by counting up; use practical and informal written methods to support the subtraction of a one-digit number from a one-digit or two-digit number and a multiple of 10 from a two-digit number	C 5 Relates subtraction to taking away	● add and subtract numbers of objects to 10 ● begin to add by counting on from the number of objects in the first set	● can use counting up to find change from 50p ● can use practical methods for subtraction effectively ● can use mental methods for subtraction such as counting on from the lower to higher number ● may keep a tally of how many counted using fingers	*I can count up to find how much I have left from 50p when I buy an object.*
④ Robot move				
Visualise and use everyday language to describe the position of objects and direction and distance when moving them, for example when placing or moving objects on a game board	SSM 5 Uses everyday words to describe position	● use everyday language to describe positions of 2D and 3D shapes ● respond to and use positional language, e.g. 'behind', under', 'on top of', 'next to', 'in between'... ● respond to and use directional language in talk about objects and movement, e.g. 'forwards', 'backwards', 'turn'	● can use appropriate vocabulary to describe position, direction and distance ● knows how to program the robot to move it in a given pathway ● can use simple maps or plans, and can find specific places or things, describing where they are	*I know how to program the robot to move around the skittles.*
⑤ Measure the box				
Estimate, measure, weigh and compare objects, choosing and using suitable uniform non-standard or standard units and measuring instruments (e.g. a lever balance, metre stick or measuring jug)	SSM 7 Uses language such as 'greater', 'smaller', 'heavier' or 'lighter' to compare quantities	● measure and order objects	● can make a good estimate of length using non-standard uniform units ● uses kilogram weights to balance heavy items and can total the weights correctly	*I can estimate how many straws I need to measure this table. I can find out how many kilogram weights I need to balance the big bag of potatoes.*

BLOCK D

Unit 3 Calculating, measuring and understanding shape

Framework objectives	Assessment focuses		Success criteria for Year 1	Learning outcomes
	Foundation stage profile scale point	Level 1		
6 Telling the time 7 Months of the year				
Use vocabulary related to time; order days of the week and months; read the time to the hour and half hour	There is no assessment focus for this level	• order events • read the time on an analogue clock at the hour and begin to know the half hour	• knows the order of the days of the week and the months of the year • knows o'clock time • knows where the minute hand will point for half past times • can tell the time for half past the hour	*I know that the big hand points to the 6 when it is half past the hour.* *I can say the months of the year in order.*
8 Turning				
Identify objects that turn about a point (e.g. scissors) or about a line (e.g. a door); recognise and make whole, half and quarter turns	SSM 5 Uses everyday words to describe position	• use everyday language to describe positions of 2D and 3D shapes • respond to and use directional language in talk about objects and movement, e.g. 'forwards', 'backwards', 'turn'	• can name some objects that turn • can make whole and half turns of themselves • can recognise half turns when following a simple plan or map • can follow directions on a simple plan or map	*I can turn myself through a number of whole and half turns.* *I can tell you some objects that turn, such as windmill sails or a water tap.*

Activities ① and ②

Prior learning
Children can work out which coins to use to pay the exact price for something. They can work out what something costs when it is half price. They can work out how many 10p badges they can buy for £1.

Framework objectives
● Solve problems involving counting, adding, subtracting, doubling or halving in the context of numbers, measures or money, for example to 'pay' and 'give change'
● Relate addition to counting on; recognise that addition can be done in any order; use practical and informal written methods to support the addition of a one-digit number or a multiple of 10 to a one-digit or two-digit number

Vocabulary
problem, method, number sentence, explain, record, count, guess, estimate, roughly, enough, not enough, too much, too little, too many, too few, more, less, the same number as, equals, add, plus, sum, total, altogether, subtract, minus, take away, difference, double, halve, half, quarter, how many?, how much? money, coin, pence, penny, pound, pay, change, buy, sell, price, spend

Resources
Worksheet: Half price
Resource sheet: Self-assessment
Classroom resources: 1p, 2p, 5p, 10p coins

① Using coins

Provide some 10p coins and ask the children to count out the relevant number of coins for given prices. Ask, for example: *How many 10p coins do I need to pay for a toy costing 40p? How did you work that out?* Repeat this for other decade amounts. Check that the children can count out the coins accurately, and that they count in tens for the coins: 10, 20, 30, 40... Decide whether to use the self-assessment sheet for the children to record their achievements and what they need to do next. They can record the number of coins needed for given prices on the sheet.

Teacher support
Less confident learners: Work with these children as a group to count up in tens for each price.
More confident learners: Ask the children to work mentally to calculate the number of coins needed.

Common misconception
Children do not relate counting in tens to using 10p coins.
Provide some 10p coins. Ask children to count with you as you touch some coins: *10, 20, 30. So this is 30p. And there are three 10p coins.* Repeat this for other quantities of 10p coins. Say together, for example: *Five 10p coins is 50p.* Repeat this over time until children are confident.

Probing questions
● Hannah buys two packets of crisps. She pays 40 pence. How much does one packet cost?
● In how many different ways can you make 30p using only silver coins?
● The badges cost 5p. How many could you buy with £1? Tell me how you worked it out.

Next steps
Support: Provide further opportunities for counting in tens and linking this to money (for example, during oral and mental starter sessions). See also Year 1 Block D Unit 2.
Extension: Challenge the children to count in 5p amounts. Ask them to find different ways of making a given amount of money using 5p then 10p coins. See also Year 2 Block D Unit 1.

② Half price

Ask the children to work in pairs to complete the worksheet 'Half price'. They take turns to choose an item for sale on the sheet, then to write the half price in the box. Their partner checks the answer, using coins.

Teacher support
Less confident learners: If the children are unsure, provide coins for them to use to find half of the price.
More confident learners: Suggest that the children work mentally to check the half price. Ask them to explain how they worked out the answers.

Common misconception
Children do not relate halving to sharing between two.
Provide some 1p coins. Ask children to count out 8p. Now ask them to share the coins equally into two groups. *How many coins are there in each group? So what is half of 8?* Repeat this for other halves of even quantities to 10, extending to beyond 10 over time.

Probing questions
● What is half of 12? How did you work that out?
● The toffee apples cost 14p each. The apples are on sale at half price. How much will you pay now for a toffee apple?

Next steps
Support: Use spinner games, where the children halve the spinner score. At first they may need counting resources, but encourage them to work mentally. See also Year 1 Block B Unit 3.
Extension: Extend the range of even numbers that the children can halve to 30. See also Year 2 Block B Unit 1.

BLOCK D

Activity ③

Prior learning
Children can count up to find how much they have left from 50p when they buy an object.

Framework objective
Understand subtraction as 'take away' and find a 'difference' by counting up; use practical and informal written methods to support the subtraction of a one-digit number from a one-digit or two-digit number and a multiple of 10 from a two-digit number

Vocabulary
money, coin, pence, penny, pound, pay, change, buy, sell, price, spend

Resources
Display page: Giving change
Resource sheet: Self-assessment
Classroom resources: 1p, 2p, 5p, 10p, 20p coins, cubes

③ Giving change

Reveal the display page 'Giving change' to the children and provide them with coins. Explain that they will have 50p to 'buy' an item from the screen and that they will need to work out the change. Choose the first item. Now ask the children to find the change from 50p by counting up using their coins. Ask them to try to use the least number of coins each time. Decide whether to use the self-assessment sheet for the children to record their achievements and what they need to do next. They can write some number sentences showing the change on the sheet.

Teacher support
Less confident learners: Provide items with prices to 10p. Ask the children to use coins to find the change. Extend to prices to 20p.
More confident learners: Provide some items with prices between 50p and £1. Ask the children to work out the change from £1, using the least number of coins.

Common misconception
Children are not confident with counting up from the price to find change.
Begin with an item that costs less than 5p. Ask children to find the change from 5p. Model this for them, for example: *3p and 2p makes 5p so that change is 2p.* It may be necessary at this stage to count in 1s. 1p coins can then be exchanged for 2p. Repeat this for something costing up to 10p. Again, encourage children to count up, using coins. Repeat this frequently over time until children are confident, then extend the price range to 20p, then to 50p.

Probing questions
● How will you check your change?
● Build me two towers that have a difference of four cubes in their heights.
● Tell me some subtraction questions that have 50p as an answer.
● Make up a question that uses the words 'difference between' and tell me how to do it.

Next steps
Support: Provide opportunities for the children to work in the class shop, as customer and as shopkeeper. Check that they give appropriate change, and use as few coins as possible to do this. See also Year 1 Block D Unit 2.
Extension: Ask the children to buy two or three things from the class shop, total their price and work out the change from £1. Tell them to use as few coins as possible. See also Year 2 Block B Unit 1.

Activity ④

Prior learning
Children know how to program the robot to move around the skittles.

Framework objective
Visualise and use everyday language to describe the position of objects and direction and distance when moving them, for example when placing or moving objects on a game board

Vocabulary
position, direction, grid, outside, inside, beside, next to, front, back, between, centre, underneath, above, on top of, below, half way, near, far, whole turn, half turn, quarter turn, right, left

Resources
Resource sheet: Self-assessment
Classroom resources: programmable toy, obstacles set out on the floor for the toy to navigate

④ Robot move

Work with a group of about four children. Provide the programmable toy and show them the obstacles on the floor. Explain to the children that you would like them to program the toy to move around the obstacles. Provide paper so that they can record the moves that they made. Decide whether to use the self-assessment sheet for the children to record their achievements and what they need to do next.

Teacher support
Less confident learners: Work together at this activity. Ask the children to say each move that they want the programmable toy to make.
More confident learners: Challenge these children to move the programmable toy through a more complicated maze.

Common misconception
Children do not know left from right.
Ask children to pretend that they are the programmable toy. Ask them to walk the route set out on the floor and to say each move that they make, such as: *Go forward for three steps. Turn right...* Use opportunities in PE for children to follow instructions that include turning left and right.

Probing questions
- How did you decide which way the robot should turn?
- How did you decide how many steps the robot needed to move to reach ___?
- Look at this map. Start at the bottom. Point to the second house on the left.

Next steps
Support: Provide further opportunities for the children to program the programmable toy. Check that they know which is left and which is right. See also Year 1 Block D Unit 2.
Extension: Ask the children to make a maze for others to program the programmable toy to move through. See also Year 2 Block D Unit 2.

BLOCK D

Activity ⑤

BLOCK D

Prior learning
Children can estimate how many straws they need to measure a table. They can find out how many kilogram weights they need to balance a big bag of potatoes. They can find out which of three objects is the heaviest by using the scales.

Framework objectives
● **Estimate, measure, weigh and compare objects, choosing and using suitable uniform non-standard or standard units and measuring instruments (e.g. a lever balance, metre stick or measuring jug)**
● Solve problems involving counting, adding, subtracting, doubling or halving in the context of numbers, measures or money, for example to 'pay' and 'give change'

Vocabulary
problem, method, number sentence, explain, record, compare, order, measure, weigh, count, guess, estimate, roughly, enough, not enough, too much, too little, too many, too few, more, long, longer, longest, short, shorter, shortest, tall, taller, tallest, light, lighter, lightest, heavy, heavier, heaviest, ruler, tape measure, metre stick, balance, scales

Resources
Worksheet: Measure the box
Classroom resources: bag of potatoes weighing about 3kg, box, three parcels labelled A, B, C, and weighing different amounts, two-pan balance scale with kilogram weights, uniform non-standard units for measuring length (for example, straws or cubes)

⑤ Measure the box

Ask the children to work in pairs to complete the worksheet 'Measure the box', which has a recording grid. Ask them to estimate first, then measure how tall the box is (using cubes) and how heavy the bag of potatoes is (using kilogram weights). The children then find which is the heaviest of three parcels. They should compare the parcels by weighing two of them each time.

Teacher support
Less confident learners: Check that the children understand that they need to estimate before they measure and that their estimates are reasonably accurate.
More confident learners: Challenge these children to order five parcels by weight by comparing them in twos using the balance.

Common misconception
Children do not use the two-pan balance in order to compare weights.
Put out two parcels and a two-pan balance. Ask children to estimate which parcel is heavier by holding it in their hands. Now place the two parcels onto the balance, one in each pan. *Which parcel is heavier? How can you tell? So which is lighter?* Add another parcel and ask children to make the comparisons again. Discuss how they know which parcel is the heaviest. Ask them to place the parcels in order of weight.

Probing questions
● Before you measure, what are the important things to remember about measuring?
● Which parcel is heaviest? How do you know?

Next steps
Support: Provide further opportunities for the children to measure weight and length. Check that they count units correctly and that they can make comparisons and order by weight or length. See also Year 1 Block C Unit 2.

Extension: Provide a box and ask the children to measure it to find its weight, length and how much it will hold. Decide whether to introduce centimetres for measuring length, tens of grams for measuring weight, and hundreds of millilitres for measuring capacity. See also Year 2 Block D Unit 1.

Activities ⑥ and ⑦

Prior learning
Children know that the big hand points to the 6 when it is half past the hour. They can say the months of the year in order.

Framework objective
Use vocabulary related to time; order days of the week and months; read the time to the hour and half hour

Vocabulary
time, clock, hands, morning, afternoon, evening, midnight, hour, night, day, week, month, year, days of the week, months and seasons of the year

Resources
Resource sheets: Clock face, Months of the year, Self-assessment
Classroom resources: teaching clock, scissors, clock stamps and ink

⑥ Telling the time

Photocopy several copies of the resource sheet 'Clock face' onto A4 card, cut out the hands and use paper fasteners to pin them to the clock face so that each child has one. Ask the children to set the clocks to the time that you say. *Set the time to 3 o'clock. Show me. Set the time to half past four. Show me.* Discuss where the hour hand goes when it is a half-past time, and check that the children show this as accurately as they can on their clocks. Then, using the teaching clock, set the time to o'clock and half-past times, and ask the children to put up their hands to tell you what time the clock says. When they have completed this activity, decide whether to use the self-assessment sheet for the children to record their achievements and what they need to do next. They can stamp some clock faces and draw hands to show some half-past times on the self-assessment sheet.

Teacher support
Less confident learners: Concentrate on o'clock times.
More confident learners: Discuss how o'clock and half-past times can be shown on a digital clock (for example, 10.00 and 10.30).

Common misconception
Children do not recognise half-past times.
Use the teaching clock. Ask children to explain where the hands would go for, say, 3 o'clock, then for 3.30, or half past three. Discuss how the large hand points to the 6 on the clock face for half-past times, as the 6 is halfway round the clock. Discuss where the little hand points, halfway past the hour and halfway to the next hour. Repeat for more half-past times, then ask children to set their clocks to the half-past times that you say.

Probing questions
- Starting at 12, which number is halfway around the clock face?
- School starts at 9 o'clock. Sam was half an hour late. Draw the time Sam arrived.
- The long hand on a clock is at 6. The small hand is between 8 and 9. What's the time?

BLOCK D

BLOCK D

▷ **Next steps**
Support: Provide further opportunities for telling the time to o'clock and half past, such as using the classroom clock to identify when it is half past. Use oral and mental starters for telling the time. See also Year 1 Block D Unit 2.
Extension: Introduce quarter past and quarter to the hour. Discuss where the hands are at these times. Talk about how, for quarter to, we say the time to the next hour. Children can find this difficult as digital time is still expressed in the same hour. See also Year 2 Block D Unit 1.

⑦ Months of the year

Provide the resource sheet 'Months of the year'. Ask the children to cut out the names of the months. Now invite them to place the months in order, starting with the first month of the year. When they have done this, ask them to choose a month in response to your questions. Ask, for example: *When is Christmas?* (December.) *Which is the month when we do not come to school?* (August.) Now ask the children to stand in a group by birthdays, so ask: *Who has a birthday in January? What is the next month? And who has a birthday then?* and so on. When the children have completed this activity, decide whether to provide them with the self-assessment sheet so that they can record their achievements and next steps.

Teacher support
Less confident learners: It may take some time for children to remember the months of the year in order, so say them together daily if possible. Link the months to events in the children's lives.
More confident learners: Encourage these children to think of something special to remember about each month.

Common misconception
Children do not know the names of the months of the year.
Ask children to say the names of the months of the year, in order, with you. This may need to be repeated many times over several days for children to remember them. Link the months with events, such as birthdays, school events or festivals, to help children to remember each one. Make a chart with children's help to show each month and what is special about it.

Probing questions
- What month is your birthday? Is it in the summer?
- Which month comes after March?
- At what time of the year do the leaves fall off the trees?

Next steps
Support: Continue to give opportunities for the children to recite the months of the year in order, until they remember them. Put the date on the board for each day. Make a special point of when the last day of the month occurs, and ask what the next month will be. See also Year 1 Block D Unit 2.
Extension: Encourage the children to know not only the names of the months but to begin to know how many days there are in each month. Teach the rhyme: *30 days hath September...* See also Year 2 Block D Unit 1.

Activity ⑧

Prior learning
Children can turn themselves through a number of whole and half turns. They can tell you some objects that turn, such as windmill sails or a water tap.

Framework objective
Identify objects that turn about a point (e.g. scissors) or about a line (e.g. a door); recognise and make whole, half and quarter turns

Vocabulary
whole turn, half turn, quarter turn, right, left, point, line

Resources
Worksheet: Turning

⑧ Turning

Ask the children to stand up. Say: *Turn to the right. Make a half turn. Which way are you facing? Turn to the front. Now how far have you turned altogether?* Check that the children understand the instructions, and can make appropriate turns. Now provide the worksheet 'Turning'. This asks the children to sort things that turn about a point, and then those that turn about a line.

Teacher support
Less confident learners: If children are unsure, place a band on their right wrists to help them to remember which is left and which is right.
More confident learners: Ask the children to look around the classroom and find other things that turn about a point or a line.

Common misconception
Children do not recognise the difference between turning about a point and about a line.
Show children a clock and a book. Discuss how the clock hands turn: that they are fixed onto a spindle in the middle of the clock. Discuss how the pages of the book turn: that they are fixed all along one edge to the spine of the book. Ask children to think of something else that turns about a point, then about a line.

Probing questions
● The big hand of the clock is pointing to the 3. What number will it point to when it has made half a turn?
● If you face the door and make half a turn, what can you then see?

Next steps
Support: During PE sessions, ask the children to make turns, left and right, and to make whole and half turns. See also Year 1 Block D Unit 2.
Extension: Challenge the children to make a routine that involves left and right, and whole and half turns. Ask them to say their routine for others to follow. See also Year 2 Block D Unit 1.

BLOCK D

These activities can be used at the end of this block to assess those children that you think have achieved the objectives.

Estimating and measuring

Objective
Estimate, measure, weigh and compare objects, choosing and using suitable uniform non-standard or standard units and measuring instruments (e.g. a lever balance, metre stick or measuring jug)

Assessment focus
Level 1: Measure and order objects using direct comparison: compare lengths directly and put them in order; respond to and use the language of comparison – longer, longest, shorter, shortest, more, less, heavier, lighter; check which of two objects is heavier/lighter and begin to put three objects into order; find objects that are longer/shorter than a metre, heavier/lighter than 500 grams, hold more/less than 1 litre
Foundation stage profile scale points: Uses language such as 'greater', 'smaller', 'heavier' or 'lighter' to compare quantities

Learning outcomes
● I can guess how many cubes will balance a parcel.
● I can use a metre stick to measure how far it is across the hall.
● I can guess how many jugs of water I will put into the bowl to fill it.
● I can use the red weights to balance a parcel.
● I can estimate how many straws I need to measure this table.
● I can find out how many kilogram weights I need to balance the big bag of potatoes.

There are three worksheets, one for each unit in this block. The activities are practical and children will need access to items for measuring and to measuring equipment. Check that the children use the equipment appropriately, and that they make sensible estimates.

1. The worksheet 'Estimating and measuring (1)' involves estimating weight and measuring to check, and using a metre stick for measuring a longer length.
2. The worksheet 'Estimating and measuring (2)' involves estimating capacity, and estimating and measuring weight.
3. The worksheet 'Estimating and measuring (3)' involves estimating and measuring length, and weighing in kilograms.

Counting paces

Objective
Count reliably at least 20 objects, recognising that when rearranged the number of objects stays the same; estimate a number of objects that can be checked by counting

Assessment focus
Level 1: Count up to 10 objects, e.g. estimate and check a number
Foundation stage profile scale points: Counts reliably up to 10 everyday objects

Learning outcome
● I can find out how long a room is by counting the paces I take to cross it.

Distribute the worksheet 'Counting paces'. Ask the children to work in pairs. They take turns to estimate how many paces they will take to cross a room, then check by pacing and counting. Their partner counts as well. They check each other's counting.

Turning

Objective
Identify objects that turn about a point (e.g. scissors) or about a line (e.g. a door); recognise and make whole, half and quarter turns

Assessment focus
Level 1: Use everyday language to describe positions of 2D and 3D shapes; respond to and use positional language, e.g. 'behind', under', 'on top of', 'next to', 'in between'…; respond to and use directional language in talk about objects and movement, e.g. 'forwards', 'backwards', 'turn'
Foundation stage profile scale points: Uses everyday words to describe position

Learning outcomes
● I know how to turn right and to turn left.
● I can turn myself through a number of whole and half turns.
● I can tell you some objects that turn, such as windmill sails or a water tap.

There are three parts to this activity. These can all be used together, or over several days.

1. Ask the children to stand up. Say: *Turn left. What are you facing? Now turn to the right. What can you see?* Check that the children recognise which way is left and which right. Repeat this several times.
2. This activity is best carried out in a large space. Ask the children to follow your instructions, for example: *Take three paces forward; turn left. What can you see? Now take four paces forward; turn right; what can you see? Turn all the way round; make a half turn.* Check that the children can follow the instructions accurately.
3. Provide the worksheet 'Turning' and a tray of items that will turn on a point and on a line (scissors, book, clock, toy car with wheels that turn, and so on). Ask the children to sort out the items and to write their name or draw them in the correct place on the worksheet.

Name	Date

Estimating and measuring (1)

1. You need a parcel, some cubes and a two-pan balance.

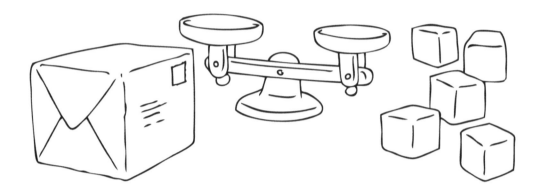

◀ Pick up the parcel.

◀ How many cubes do you think will balance the parcel?

_____

◀ Weigh the parcel.

◀ How many cubes did you need to balance the parcel?

_____

◀ Did you make a good guess? _____

2. You need a metre stick.

◀ Measure how wide the hall is.

◀ How many metres wide is the hall?

_____

How easy?

Red
Amber
Green

How do you think you have done?

_____

_____

Name   Date

Counting paces

Work with a partner.

1. Take turns to estimate how many paces you will need to cross the room.

◢ Write your estimate here:

_____

2. Now count the paces you take to cross the room. Your partner counts too.

◢ Write the number of paces you took here:

_____

◢ Write how many paces your partner counted here:

_____

◢ Did you count the same number as your partner? _____

◢ Did you make a good estimate? _____

How easy?

Red

Amber

Green

How do you think you have done?

_____

_____

Name   Date

Turning

You will need the tray of things from your teacher.

- Find the things that turn on a point.
- Find the things that turn on a line.
- Draw them in the spaces below.

Things that turn on a point

Things that turn on a line

How easy?

Red

Amber

Green

How do you think you have done?

_____

_____

BLOCK E
Securing number facts, relationships and calculating

Expected prior learning
Check that children can already:
- use developing mathematical ideas and methods to solve practical problems involving counting, measuring, comparing, ordering, adding, subtracting or partitioning objects
- describe solutions to practical problems, talking about their own ideas, methods and choices
- talk about, recognise and recreate simple patterns
- count aloud in ones, twos, fives or tens
- select two groups of objects to make a given total of objects
- relate addition to combining two groups of objects and subtraction to 'taking away', and use the related vocabulary
- count repeated groups of the same size
- share objects into equal groups and count how many in each group.

Objectives overview
The text in this diagram identifies the focus of mathematics learning within the block.

Key aspects of learning
- Information processing
- Problem solving
- Motivation

Describing patterns and relationships involving numbers or shapes and testing examples that fit conditions

Solving problems involving counting, adding, subtracting, doubling or halving of numbers, measures or money

Representing and interpreting problems using numbers, practical materials and diagrams

BLOCK E: Securing number facts, relationships and calculating

Counting on and back in 1s, 2s, 5s, 10s

Combining groups of 2, 5, 10; sharing in equal groups

Doubles of numbers to 10

Halves and quarters in context

Describing and recording addition and subtraction number sentences

BLOCK E

Unit 1 ■ Securing number facts, relationships and calculating

Introduction

In this unit, children should be encouraged to explain how they have solved problems. Ask them to explain in the order in which they carried out their work. Also encourage them to record their results (for example, by writing a number sentence). They continue to count, extending this to include counting in twos and tens. They find halves of objects and small quantities and doubles of quantities. They begin to recognise that, for example, half of 8 is 4 and double 4 is 8. They continue to use practical and mental methods for addition and subtraction, including counting on in ones, using cubes and counting on a number line.

Framework objectives	Assessment focuses		Success criteria for Year 1	Learning outcomes
	Foundation stage profile scale point	Level 1		
① Number problems				
Describe a puzzle or problem using numbers, practical materials and diagrams; use these to solve the problem and set the solution in the original context	NLC 8 Uses developing mathematical ideas and methods to solve practical problems	• represent their work with objects or pictures • discuss their work, e.g. with support • respond to questions and ideas from peers and adults • refer to the materials they have used and talk about what they have done, patterns they have noticed, etc • draw simple conclusions from their work, e.g. with support • explain numbers and calculations, how many altogether, how many used or hidden, how many left, how many each, etc	• can describe how a problem was solved • can use numbers and objects to help with solving the problem	I can talk about how I solved a problem using numbers and objects to help me.
② Add and subtract				
Use the vocabulary related to addition and subtraction and symbols to describe and record addition and subtraction number sentences	C 6 In practical activities and discussion, begins to use the vocabulary involved in adding and subtracting	• draw simple conclusions from their work, e.g. with support • explain numbers and calculations, how many altogether, how many used or hidden, how many left, how many each, etc	• can use addition or subtraction vocabulary in a practical context • can give the solution as a number sentence, using addition or subtraction vocabulary	I can describe an addition or subtraction using mathematical words (in a practical context).

BLOCK E

Unit 1 📖 Securing number facts, relationships and calculating

Framework objectives	Assessment focuses		Success criteria for Year 1	Learning outcomes
	Foundation stage profile scale point	**Level 1**		
③ Counting patterns				
Count on or back in ones, twos, fives and tens and use this knowledge to derive the multiples of 2, 5 and 10 to the tenth multiple	NLC 4 Says number names in order	• order numbers to 10 • say what number comes next, is one more/less • count back to zero • place 1–10 into ascending order • point to first, second, etc. in a line • begin to count in twos	• can count on and back in ones from zero to at least 20 • can continue a count from any small number in ones • can count on and back in twos from zero to 20 • can count on and back in tens from zero to 100 • with help, can count in fives	*I can count on and back in ones and tens. I am beginning to count in fives.*
④ Double me!				
Recall the doubles of all numbers to at least 10	C 4 Relates addition by combining two groups	• begin to know some addition facts, e.g. • doubles of numbers to double 5	• can use mental methods such as counting on to find doubles to 5 + 5 • 'knows' some or all doubles to 5 + 5	*I can recall or work out doubles of numbers to 5 + 5.*
⑤ Finding half				
Use the vocabulary of halves and quarters in context	C 6 In practical activities and discussion, begins to use the vocabulary involved in adding and subtracting	• begin to use the fraction, one-half, e.g. • halve shapes including folding paper shapes, lengths of string • put water in a clear container so that it is about 'half-full' • halve an even number of objects	• can find half of a small number of objects in a practical context • can find half of an item such as a ribbon or sheet of paper by folding and cutting	*I can find half of a piece of paper or string, or half a shape. I can find half of a small number of objects.*

Activity ①

Prior learning Children can talk about how they solved a problem using numbers and objects to help them.	**Framework objective** Describe a puzzle or problem using numbers, practical materials and diagrams; use these to solve the problem and set the solution in the original context **Vocabulary** problem, solution, calculate, calculation, number sentence, answer, method, explain, pattern, order **Resources** **Resource sheet:** Self-assessment **Classroom resources:** counting materials (such as blocks)

① Number problems

Work with a group of about six children. Provide counting materials, such as blocks. Explain that you are going to give the children a problem. Say: *I have four cats and two dogs. How many animals is that altogether?* Ask the children to show you how they solved the problem. Ask another: *Here are six blocks. How many more do I need to make eight? How did you work that out?* Decide whether to use the self-assessment sheet for the children to record their achievements and what they need to do next. They could draw pictures or use numbers to show how they worked out the problem.

Teacher support
Less confident learners: Simplify the problems, keeping the totals to up to 6.
More confident learners: Pose problems with totals to 10.

Common misconception
Children count all rather than counting on.
Show children three cubes. *How many more do I need to make four?* Invite them to say how they would find out. Check that they remember that they already have three cubes so that there is no need to count the three again. Encourage them to count on from three to four. Repeat for other small totals.

Probing questions
● Look at this problem. What do you have to find out or do?
● What does your drawing tell us?
● There are six people on the bus. Three more get on. How many people are on the bus now? Use these cubes. Show me what to do.

Next steps
Support: Limit the range of totals for problems to up to 10. See also Foundation Stage Overview of Learning 5.
Extension: Extend the totals to beyond 10. See also Year 2 Block E Unit 2.

BLOCK E

Activity ②

Prior learning
Children can describe an addition or subtraction using mathematical words (in a practical context).

Framework objective
Use the vocabulary related to addition and subtraction and symbols to describe and record addition and subtraction number sentences

Vocabulary
problem, solution, calculate, calculation, number sentence, answer, method, explain, pattern, order, add, subtract, sum, total, altogether, difference, plus, minus, equals

Resources
Display page: Add and subtract
Resource sheet: Self-assessment
Classroom resources: cubes

② Add and subtract

Provide cubes for the children to model the problem. Reveal the display page 'Add and subtract'. Ask the children to read the first word problem with you. Ask them to work out the answer. Invite a child to say a number sentence to fit the problem, such as: *4 add 2 equals 6*. Repeat this for the other problems on the subsequent display pages. Decide whether to use the self-assessment sheet for the children to record their achievements and what they need to do next.

Teacher support
Less confident learners: Work together as a group. Model each problem and check that the children count on/back rather than counting all each time.
More confident learners: Challenge these children to solve the problems mentally, by counting on/back.

Common misconception
Children count all rather than counting on/back.
Show children three cubes. *How many more do I need to make four? How can you find out?* Check that children remember that they have three cubes so that there is no need to count the three again. Encourage them to count on from 3 to 4. Repeat for other small totals. Repeat for subtraction. Check that children remove the correct amount, and then count what is left. So, for 6 subtract 2, they can count back 2 and then say what is left. *6, 5, 4. So there are four cubes left.*

Probing questions
● How would you show someone an easy way to find 3 more than a number? What about 3 less? Is there another way?
● What is the sum/total?
● What is the difference between these two numbers?
● Make up a 'take away' question. Show me what to do.

Next steps
Support: Provide addition and subtraction activities for totals to about 5, so that the children feel confident with these. Then extend to totals to about 10. See also Year 1 Block A Unit 1.
Extension: Encourage the children to work mentally. Ask them to explain how they found the answer so that others in the class hear about the mental process. See also Year 1 Block A Unit 2.

BLOCK E

Activity ③

Prior learning Children can count on and back in ones and tens. They have begun to count in fives.	**Framework objective** Count on or back in ones, twos, fives and tens and use this knowledge to derive the multiples of 2, 5 and 10 to the tenth multiple **Vocabulary** count in twos, fives, tens **Resources** **Worksheet:** Counting patterns

③ Counting patterns

Ask the children to count with you in 2s to 20, and then back again. Keep the pace sharp. Repeat this for counting in tens to 100 and back again. Ask the children to count with you in fives from 0 to 50 and back again. Observe how well the children manage this. Say the numbers in the count in fives and help the children to say the next number if they stumble. Provide the worksheet 'Counting patterns', which has patterns in twos and tens. Invite the children to say each counting pattern before they write in the missing numbers.

Teacher support
Less confident learners: Concentrate on counting in twos at this stage.
More confident learners: Ask the children to write out the counting in 5s pattern for as far as they can remember.

Common misconception
Children do not remember the counting in 2s or 10s patterns.
Say the twos pattern together. Note where children stumble. Write the numbers 0 to 10 on the board and ask children to help you to find the counting in twos numbers. Circle these and ask children to count to 10 and back in twos. When they are confident with this, extend the count to 20 and back. Use a 100-square to show children the tens numbers and repeat the activity, counting forward and back.

Probing questions
- How far can you count in fives?
- 20, 30, 40... Count on to 70.
- 60, 50, 40, 30. What numbers come next in the sequence?
- I will clap where a number is missing: 10, 20, 30, [one clap], 50, 60. Tell me the missing number.

Next steps
Support: Count together in twos, fives and tens during oral and mental starters. See also Foundation Stage Overview of Learning 5.
Extension: Encourage the children to say the counting patterns without you. Check that they can say these confidently. See also Year 1 Block E Unit 2.

BLOCK E

Activity

Prior learning Children can recall or work out doubles of numbers to 5 + 5.	**Framework objective** Recall the doubles of all numbers to at least 10 **Vocabulary** double **Resources** **Resource sheet:** Self-assessment **Classroom resources:** double dominoes 1 + 1 to 5 + 5

④ Double me!

Work with a group of about six children. Say a number for them to double, from 1 to 5. They write a number sentence, such as 2 + 2 = 4. Ask the children to explain how they found the answer. Decide whether to use the self-assessment sheet for the children to record their achievements and what they need to do next. They can record their doubles number sentences on the sheet.

Teacher support
Less confident learners: Provide the double dominoes. Ask the children to say the doubles. If they are unsure, they can count the spots. Check that they count on – for example, for double 2: *2 and 3, 4.*
More confident learners: Extend the range of doubles you ask to 10 + 10.

Common misconception
Children do not understand how to double a number.
Provide some cubes. Ask children to count out one cube and one cube. *What is double 1?* Check that children understand that double 1 is the same as 1 plus 1. If they are still unsure, ask them to total how many cubes there are. Repeat this for each of the doubles to 5 + 5. Encourage children to count on from one set of cubes to the next: *3 and 4, 5, 6. So double 3 is 6.*

Probing questions
● Roll this dice and double your number. What score do you get?
● Look at these domino doubles. How many spots are there altogether?

Next steps
Support: Include some doubling in oral and mental starters. See also Foundation Stage Overview of Learning 5.
Extension: Continue to encourage the children to learn doubles to 10 + 10. See also Year 1 Block B Unit 2.

BLOCK E

Activity ⑤

Prior learning Children can find half of a small number of objects.	**Framework objective** Use the vocabulary of halves and quarters in context **Vocabulary** fraction, half, half way between, halve, whole **Resources** **Worksheet:** Finding half **Classroom resources:** cubes

⑤ Finding half

Provide the worksheet 'Finding half'. This contains pictures of insects. The children count how many there are, write that number, then find half and write that number too. At the foot of the sheet there are two number sentences to be completed, one for doubling and one for halving. Check how the children find half of a number.

Teacher support
Less confident learners: Provide cubes for the children to use as they count. They can count out how many things there are in the first picture, count that number of cubes, and then, by sharing, find half.
More confident learners: Encourage the children to find half mentally. Ask them how they worked this out.

Common misconception
Children do not have a strategy for finding half of a small quantity.
Count out six cubes. *How can we find half of these?* Demonstrate how to share them into two sets. Repeat this for other quantities until children are confident.

Probing questions
- Show me half a page, half a ribbon, half of these six eggs.
- Give me half of the pencils in the pot.

Next steps
Support: Give the children further experience of finding half of small quantities, using practical materials. See also Foundation Stage Overview of Learning 10.
Extension: Encourage the children to 'know' half of small quantities. Extend this to quantities up to 20. See also Year 1 Block E Unit 2.

BLOCK E

Unit 2 Securing number facts, relationships and calculating

Introduction

In this unit, children develop their ability to solve problems and puzzles including money problems. They should be encouraged to listen and to give their views about how information has been presented. They develop their skills in addition and subtraction, counting in twos, fives and tens, and begin to understand about multiples and how these can be calculated using their counting skills. They recall doubles of numbers to 10 and find their halves, as well as finding halves of shapes. They combine equal groups of 2, 5 and 10 to find the total, and share into equal groups in order to find how many in each group.

Framework objectives	Assessment focuses		Success criteria for Year 1	Learning outcomes
	Foundation stage profile scale point	Level 1		
① Solving problems				
Describe a puzzle or problem using numbers, practical materials and diagrams; use these to solve the problem and set the solution in the original context	NLC 8 Uses developing mathematical ideas and methods to solve practical problems	• represent their work with objects or pictures • discuss their work, e.g. with support • respond to questions and ideas from peers and adults • refer to the materials they have used and talk about what they have done, patterns they have noticed, etc.	• can use objects to show how a problem was solved • can make a drawing to show how a problem was solved • can explain how the objects or drawing helped in solving the problem	*I can show how I solved a problem using drawings or objects to help me.*
② Measuring problems				
Solve problems involving counting, adding, subtracting, doubling or halving in the context of numbers, measures or money, for example to 'pay' and 'give change'	C 8 Uses developing mathematical ideas and methods to solve practical problems	• solve addition/subtraction problems involving up to 10 objects, e.g. • solve measuring problems such as how many balance with...	• can use counting to help to solve measurement problems • can calculate to solve measurement problems	*I can count and calculate to solve measurement problems.*
③ Writing number sentences				
Use the vocabulary related to addition and subtraction and symbols to describe and record addition and subtraction number sentences	C 6 In practical activities and discussion, begins to use the vocabulary involved in adding and subtracting	• record their work, e.g. • record their work with objects, pictures or diagrams • begin to use the symbols '+' and '=' to record additions	• can record an addition or subtraction number sentence, using signs (+, -, =) appropriately • can explain what the number sentence means	*I can record an addition or subtraction number sentence and tell you what it means.*

Unit 2 ⬜ Securing number facts, relationships and calculating

Framework objectives	Assessment focuses		Success criteria for Year 1	Learning outcomes
	Foundation stage profile scale point	Level 1		
④ Counting				
Count on or back in ones, twos, fives and tens and use this knowledge to derive the multiples of 2, 5 and 10 to the tenth multiple	NLC 4 Says number names in order	● order numbers to 10 ● say what number comes next, is one more/less ● count back to zero ● place 1–10 into ascending order ● point to first, second, etc in a line ● begin to count in twos	● can count on and back from zero in ones, twos, fives and tens ● can find the next number in a series that begins on any number up to about 30 for counting in ones, up to about 20 for counting in twos, up to about 50 for counting in fives, and any number from zero to 100 for counting tens	*I can count on and back in ones, fives and tens.*
⑤ Equal shares				
Solve practical problems that involve combining groups of 2, 5 or 10, or sharing into equal groups	C 6 In practical activities and discussion, begins to use the vocabulary involved in adding and subtracting	● begin to use the fraction, one-half, e.g. ● halve an even number of objects	● knows how many equal groups to make ● can share objects into equal groups ● can use counting to find how many are in one group	*I can share objects into equal groups and work out how many in one group.*
⑥ Doubles word problems				
Recall the doubles of all numbers to at least 10	C 4 Relates addition by combining two groups	● begin to know some addition facts, e.g. ● doubles of numbers to double 5	● can use mental methods such as counting on to find doubles of all numbers to 10 + 10 ● 'knows' some or all of the doubles to 10 + 10	*I can recall or work out doubles of all numbers to 10.*
⑦ Halves, quarters and wholes				
Use the vocabulary of halves and quarters in context	C 6 In practical activities and discussion, begins to use the vocabulary involved in adding and subtracting	● begin to use the fraction, one-half, e.g. ● halve shapes including folding paper shapes, lengths of string ● halve an even number of objects	● can use the vocabulary of halves and quarters in context ● can make whole, half and quarter turns on the spot ● can fold a sheet of paper to make halves and quarters ● knows that two equal groups must be made in order to find half of a number of objects ● can find half of a number of objects by sharing them into two equal groups	*I can make whole, half and quarter turns on the spot.* *I can fold a piece of paper into halves and quarters.* *I can find half of a number of objects by sharing them into two equal groups.*

■SCHOLASTIC

Activity ①

Prior learning
Children can show how they solved a problem using drawings or objects to help them.

Framework objective
Describe a puzzle or problem using numbers, practical materials and diagrams; use these to solve the problem and set the solution in the original context

Vocabulary
problem, solution, calculate, calculation, number sentence, answer, method, explain, pattern, order, compare, more, less, how many more/less?

Resources
Display page: Solving problems
Resource sheet: 0-30 number line, Self-assessment
Classroom resources: counting materials

① Solving problems

Reveal the display page 'Solving problems' and provide the resource sheet '0-30 number line' and counting materials. Show the first problem. Ask the children to solve the problem. Invite some children to explain what they did and compare answers. Go to the second display page and repeat the steps for the next problem. Encourage the children to write a number sentence with the answer where appropriate. Decide whether to use the self-assessment sheet for the children to record their achievements and what they need to do next.

Teacher support
Less confident learners: Work with these children as a small group. Simplify the problems by choosing smaller numbers if necessary.
More confident learners: Encourage these children to work mentally. Ask them to explain how they calculated.

Common misconception
Children do not recognise the key words in a problem.
Read the second problem together. *Do you think this is an addition or subtraction problem? Which word helps you to know?* (altogether.) *So how do we find the answer?* Repeat this for the other problems, each time identifying key words and their meanings.

Probing questions
● Give me a number between 6 and 12. Is it closer to 6 or 12? Show me how you know using this number line.
● How many animals altogether are there in the three fields? Explain how you worked out your answer.

Next steps
Support: Provide further opportunities for solving word problems. Ask the children to identify the word or words that help them to know what type of problem it is. See also Foundation Stage Overview of Learning 8.
Extension: Ask the children to explain clearly to the other children how they solved a problem. Ask, for example: *How did you know that you needed to add/ subtract for this problem?* See also Year 1 Block E Unit 2.

Activity ②

Prior learning
Children can count and calculate to solve measurement problems.

Framework objective
Solve problems involving counting, adding, subtracting, doubling or halving in the context of numbers, measures or money, for example to 'pay' and 'give change'

Vocabulary
problem, solution, calculate, calculation, number sentence, answer, method, explain, pattern, order, compare, more, less, how many more/less?, add, subtract, sum, total, altogether, difference, plus, minus, equals

Resources
Worksheet: Measuring problems

② Measuring problems

Ask the children to solve the problems on the worksheet 'Measuring problems'. The problems involve addition, subtraction and counting. Read each problem through with the children and look at the pictures. Give them time to solve the problem, then encourage them to explain how they solved each problem.

Teacher support
Less confident learners: Work as a small group. Check that the children understand what sort of problem each is. Provide counting materials if necessary.
More confident learners: Suggest that these children work mentally, and explain to the others how they solved each problem.

Common misconception
Children do not recognise the relevant vocabulary in a problem.
Read the first problem together and look at the pictures. Ask children to find the key words in the problem and count the cubes in the pictures. Discuss what sort of problem it is and ask children to solve it. Provide practical materials to help them. Repeat this for the other problems, checking each time that children recognise the key words.

Probing questions
● What do you need to find out? How do you know you need to add/subtract/double/halve?
● What helped you to decide how to do this calculation? Could you do it another way?
● How many different pairs of numbers can you remember that have a total of 10?

Next steps
Support: Provide further opportunities, in practical situations, to solve problems. For example, ask the children to measure the lengths of two ribbons. They can find the total length and the difference in length between the two pieces. See also Year 1 Block A Unit 2.
Extension: Challenge the children to find larger totals and differences of measurements. See also Year 1 Block A Unit 3.

Activity ③

Prior learning
Children can record an addition or subtraction number sentence and say what it means.

Framework objective
Use the vocabulary related to addition and subtraction and symbols to describe and record addition and subtraction number sentences

Vocabulary
add, subtract, sum, total, altogether, difference, plus, minus, equals

Resources
Worksheet: Writing number sentences

③ Writing number sentences

Provide the worksheet 'Writing number sentences'. Ask the children to write the number sentences, putting in the appropriate symbols as well as numbers. When they have finished the sheet, ask them to explain their number sentences, telling you what the numbers and symbols represent.

Teacher support
Less confident learners: Work as a group to find solutions. Encourage the children to write number sentences, using numbers and symbols in the correct order, and to explain what these mean.
More confident learners: Challenge these children to use larger numbers for the open number sentences.

Common misconception
Children are unable to write number sentences using symbols.
Say a number sentence together, such as: *4 add 2 equals 6.* As children say this with you, write it on the board. Point to each number and symbol and say the sentence together. Repeat this for more addition sentences, and ask children to write these themselves. Repeat this for subtraction sentences.

Probing questions
● Using a number line, show me two numbers that have a difference of 2. How might you write that?
● What numbers can make these statements true? ___ is one more than ___, ___ is 10 less than ___.
● How did you decide what numbers to use?

Next steps
Support: Provide further opportunities for writing number sentences, using numbers and symbols, such as writing a number sentence to fit with a word problem. See also Year 1 Block A Unit 2.
Extension: Include a range of number sentences with larger numbers. Check that the children are clear about how to write teen numbers. See also Year 1 Block A Unit 3.

BLOCK E

Activity ④

Prior learning Children can count on and back in ones, fives and tens.	**Framework objective** Count on or back in ones, twos, fives and tens and use this knowledge to derive the multiples of 2, 5 and 10 to the tenth multiple

Vocabulary
count, count up to, count on from, count on to, count in ones, twos, fives, tens

Resources
Resource sheet: Self-assessment
Classroom resources: elastic bands, straws

④ Counting

Work with a group of about six children. Ask them to count together, in ones, twos, fives and tens, forwards and back, from zero. Stop the count and say: *What comes next? What was the number before the one you just said? Listen to this count: 22, 23, 24; what number comes next? And next?* Repeat this for all of the counts. Provide the children with some straws and elastic bands. *Count 60 using bundles of tens. How many bundles did you need to make?* Repeat this for other multiples of tens. Decide whether to use the self-assessment sheet for the children to record their achievements and what they need to do next.

Teacher support
Less confident learners: Limit the counting to counting in ones and twos at this stage.
More confident learners: Encourage these children to count quickly as well as accurately.

Common misconception
Children do not recognise the next number in counts of 2, instead saying the 'one more' number.
Use counting rhymes that involve counting in twos (for example: *Two, four, six, eight, who do we appreciate?*). Then say the numbers together, keeping a good rhythm to the count. Repeat this many times, both counting forwards and back until children are confident. It may help to link this to odd and even numbers, demonstrating this using cubes.

Probing questions
● Is there a quick way of finding a number that is 10 more than a number? What about 10 less?
● What comes next: 25, 26, 27...; 22, 21, 20...; 90, 80, 70...
● Make up another counting pattern for others to solve.

Next steps
Support: Extend the counting to include fives and tens as the children become confident with counting in ones and twos. See also Year 1 Block E Unit 1.
Extension: Encourage the children to continue the counts up to 100. See also Year 1 Block E Unit 3.

Activity ⑤

Prior learning
Children can share objects into equal groups and work out how many in one group.

Framework objective
Solve practical problems that involve combining groups of 2, 5 or 10, or sharing into equal groups

Vocabulary
double, group, groups of, share

Resources
Resource sheet: Self-assessment
Classroom resources: cubes, paper plates or empty margarine tubs

⑤ Equal shares

Work with a group of six to eight children. Provide each child with five paper plates and 20 cubes. Say: *There are two children who want to share six cubes. How many will they have each?* Check that the children take two plates and six cubes. Repeat: *Three children want to share 12 cubes. How many will they have each? Five children want to share 20 cubes. How many will they have each?* and so on. Once they have completed this activity, decide whether to use the self-assessment sheet for the children to record their achievements and what they need to do next. They can record one of their sharings by drawing the paper plates as circles and the cubes shared equally on them.

Teacher support
Less confident learners: At first, keep to sharing between two plates until it is clear that children understand how to make equal shares.
More confident learners: Decide whether to increase the number of plates to six, and the number of cubes to 30.

Common misconception
Children do not make equal groups when sharing.
Ask two children to share out six cubes so that they have an equal amount each. Observe their strategy for sharing. Show them, if necessary, how to share by the 'one for you and one for me' method. Repeat this for other quantities, until children show that they understand that both amounts shared out must have equal quantities. Extend to sharing between three, and so on.

Probing questions
● How many fingers are there altogether on six hands?
● There are ten crayons in three boxes. How many crayons are there altogether?
● How many 2p coins make 20p?

Next steps
Support: Use practical contexts, such as sharing out some pennies equally among a small group of children, who then use the money to buy things in the class shop. See also Foundation Stage Overview of Learning 10.
Extension: Encourage the children to link counting in groups to sharing into groups. See also Year 1 Block E Unit 3.

BLOCK E

Activity ⑥

| **Prior learning**
Children can recall or work out doubles of all numbers to 10. | **Framework objective**
Recall the doubles of all numbers to at least 10

Vocabulary
double

Resources
Resource sheet: Self-assessment
Classroom resources: cubes |

⑥ Doubles word problems

Explain that you will say some doubles word problems. Ask the children to work mentally if they can (alternatively, they can use the cubes or a number line). They can record the doubles as addition sentences on the back of the self-assessment sheet (for example, 3 + 3 = 6). Say, for example: *There are two pots of five pencils. How many pencils are there altogether? Sarah eats three sweets, then another three sweets. How many sweets did she eat in total? Joshua has six toy cars. Ellie also has six toy cars. How many have they altogether?* and so on.

Teacher support
Less confident learners: Try doubles to 5 + 5 to at first, extending to up to 10 + 10 over time.
More confident learners: Ask doubling and halving questions.

Common misconception
Children do not understand that doubling can be found by addition.
Model a doubling question using towers of cubes. *Here is a tower of three cubes. Here is another tower of three cubes. How many cubes are there altogether? How can we find out?* Discuss how this can be found by addition: 3 + 3 = 6. Repeat this with other doubles. Check that children count on to find the answer: *3 and 4, 5, 6.*

Probing questions
● What is 6 + 6? What is double 6?
● What number must I double to get 10?

Next steps
Support: Include doubling problems in oral and mental starters. Encourage the children to commit to memory the doubles to 5 + 5, then to 10 + 10. See also Year 1 Block B Unit 2.
Extension: Include some double plus 1 questions in oral and mental starters. For example, ask: *What is 5 + 6? 9 + 8?* (and so on). See also Year 1 Block B Unit 3.

BLOCK E

Activity ⑦

Prior learning
Children can make whole, half and quarter turns on the spot. They can fold a piece of paper into halves and quarters. They can find half of a number of objects by sharing them into two equal groups.

Framework objective
Use the vocabulary of halves and quarters in context

Vocabulary
fraction, half, half way between, halve, quarter, whole

Resources
Worksheet: Halves, quarters and wholes
Classroom resources: paper

⑦ Halves, quarters and wholes

This activity can be completed as part of a PE lesson. Ask the children to stand up. *Turn on the spot all the way around. Turn halfway to your left/right. Make a whole turn.* Invite them to take turns to give similar instructions for a partner to follow. Next, provide each child with a sheet of paper. *Fold the paper in half. Open it out. How many halves are there? How many halves make a whole? Fold your paper into quarters. How many quarters are there? How many quarters make a whole?* Finally, provide the children with the worksheet 'Halves, quarters and wholes' and ask them to complete it individually.

Teacher support
Less confident learners: If the children find it difficult to find half of the pictures on the worksheet, ask them to count the items, then count out that number of cubes, and find half by sharing.
More confident learners: Challenge these children to find quarters of up to about 20 objects.

Common misconception
Children do not make equal groups when finding half.
Ask two children to take half each of a set of six cubes. Watch how they share these out. Check that they make equal groups, and how they do this. If necessary, ask them to share the items equally – 'one for you and one for me' and so on. Repeat for other even-numbered quantities until children are confident with making equal groups.

Probing questions
● How will you find half of that circle?
● How will you find half of these counters?
● Which of these shapes is more than half shaded?
● Here is a set of 12 pencils. How many is half the set?

Next steps
Support: Provide an even number of items for the children to share into halves. Check how they share them and that they understand that they must always make equal shares. See also Year 1 Block E Unit 1.
Extension: Ask the children to begin to work mentally to find halves of quantities. Relate this to their knowledge of doubles and halves. See also Year 1 Block E Unit 3.

BLOCK E

Unit 3 ◾ Securing number facts, relationships and calculating

Introduction

In this unit, children should be encouraged to work together and to decide how they will carry out each task, how they will record the results and how they will report back to the rest of the class. They solve problems, find solutions to puzzles and describe patterns and relationships involving numbers. They develop their counting skills in ones, twos, fives and tens, and use these skills in order to identify multiples of 2, 5 and 10. They find doubles of numbers, and halves, in practical contexts. They solve problems involving sharing or counting to find multiples.

Framework objectives	Assessment focuses		Success criteria for Year 1	Learning outcomes
	Foundation stage profile scale point	Level 1		
① Make 20p				
Describe a puzzle or problem using numbers, practical materials and diagrams; use these to solve the problem and set the solution in the original context	NLC 8 Uses developing mathematical ideas and methods to solve practical problems	• represent their work with objects or pictures • discuss their work, e.g. with support • respond to questions and ideas from peers and adults • refer to the materials they have used and talk about what they have done, patterns they have noticed, etc • draw simple conclusions from their work, e.g. with support • describe the different ways they have sorted objects, what is the same about objects in a set, how sets differ • identify which set has most, which object is biggest, smallest, tallest, etc • explain numbers and calculations, how many altogether, how many used or hidden, how many left, how many each, etc	• can work cooperatively and collaboratively with a partner or in a small group • helps to decide how to solve a problem • helps to decide on the best way to describe the findings • can use numbers, practical materials and/ or diagrams to help to explain the solution in the original context	*I can work with a partner or in a small group to decide the best way to describe what we found out.*
② Making patterns				
Describe simple patterns and relationships involving numbers or shapes; decide whether examples satisfy given conditions	C 4 Relates addition by combining two groups	• recognise and use a simple pattern or relationship, e.g. with support • copy and continue a simple pattern of objects, shapes or numbers	• can make a pattern from shapes and can explain how it would continue • can make a pattern from numbers and can explain how it would continue • can look at a pattern, decide what is wrong with it, and correct it	*I can describe a pattern made from shapes or numbers and tell you how it would continue.*

Unit 3 ▢ Securing number facts, relationships and calculating

Framework objectives	Assessment focuses		Success criteria for Year 1	Learning outcomes
	Foundation stage profile scale point	Level 1		
③ Counting in ones, twos, fives and tens				
Count on or back in ones, twos, fives and tens and use this knowledge to derive the multiples of 2, 5 and 10 to the tenth multiple	NLC 4 Says number names in order	● order numbers to 10 ● say what number comes next, is one more/less ● count back to zero ● place 1–10 into ascending order ● point to first, second, etc in a line ● begin to count in twos	● can count from and back to zero in ones (to at least 30), twos (to at least 20), tens (to one hundred) and fives (to 50) ● recognises sequences of ones, twos, fives and tens, and can continue them ● can find missing numbers in a sequence of ones, twos, fives and tens	*I can count on from or back to zero in ones, twos, fives or tens.*
④ Groups				
Solve practical problems that involve combining groups of 2, 5 or 10, or sharing into equal groups	C 8 Uses developing mathematical ideas and methods to solve practical problems	● begin to use the fraction, one-half, e.g. ● halve an even number of objects	● can use a number line to count in twos, fives or tens ● can solve problems that involve combining groups of twos, fives or tens, using practical materials or number lines ● recognises how many groups to share into for making equal groups ● can solve problems that involve sharing into equal groups of twos, fives or tens	*I can find how many there are in several groups of 2, 5 or 10.* *I can share objects into equal groups and tell you how many there are in one group.*
⑤ Doubles				
Recall the doubles of all numbers to at least 10	C 4 Relates addition by combining two groups	● begin to know some addition facts, e.g. ● doubles of numbers to double 5	● can recall the doubles of all numbers to at least 10, or use mental methods to find the solutions, such as counting on ● can use known doubles to find other doubles ● can explain how the solution to new doubles was found	*I can recall or work out doubles of numbers to at least 10.* *I can use doubles I know to help me work out other doubles.*

Unit 3 ⬛ Securing number facts, relationships and calculating

Framework objectives	Assessment focuses		Success criteria for Year 1	Learning outcomes
	Foundation stage profile scale point	Level 1		
6 Halves and quarters				
Use the vocabulary of halves and quarters in context	C 6 In practical activities and discussion, begins to use the vocabulary involved in adding and subtracting	• begin to use the fraction, one-half, e.g. • put water in a clear container so that it is about 'half-full' • order events • read the time on an analogue clock at the hour and begin to know the half hour • begin to use the fraction, one-half, e.g. • halve an even number of objects	• knows and uses the vocabulary of halves and quarters in context • can find half of volumes by pouring • knows half past times • can find a quarter of a number of objects by sharing them into four equal groups	*I can find half of the water in a jug by pouring it into two glasses so that each glass has the same amount.* *I can tell you when the clock says half past 2.* *I can find a quarter of a number of objects by sharing them into four equal groups.*

Activity ①

Prior learning
Children can work with a partner or in a small group to decide the best way to describe what they found out.

Framework objective
Describe a puzzle or problem using numbers, practical materials and diagrams; use these to solve the problem and set the solution in the original context

Vocabulary
problem, solution, calculate, calculation, number sentence, answer, method, explain,

Resources
Resource sheet: Self-assessment
Classroom resources: 1p, 2p, 5p, 10p and 20p coins

① Make 20p

Ask the children to work with a partner. Explain that they are going to use coins to find three ways to make 20p. Ask them to find a way to record what they find out, and that they should be ready to explain what they did to others. When they have finished, ask them to work with another pair and to explain what they found out and how they recorded their work. Decide whether to use the self-assessment sheet for the children to record their achievements and what they need to do next.

Teacher support
Less confident learners: Make the total 10p, and remove the 10p and 20p coins.
More confident learners: Make the total 40p.

Common misconception
Children do not understand the value of the coins, and sees all coins as worth '1'.
Ask children to count out the appropriate number of penny coins for a 2p, and then a 5p coin. Discuss how it is easier to carry around one 5p coin than five 1p coins. Now ask children to find different ways of making 5p, using the 1p and 2p coins. Repeat this over time for the 10p coin.

Probing questions
● I want to buy one banana. I have 20p. The banana costs 35p. How much more money do I need? Explain your method.
● I buy two stickers. Tell me how much it will cost for both stickers. Now find the right coins to pay for the stickers.

Next steps
Support: Over time, extend the range of coins used to 20p. See also Year 1 Block E Unit 2.
Extension: Challenge the children to find different ways of making 50p. See also Year 2 Block E Unit 1.

BLOCK E

Activity ②

Prior learning
Children can describe a pattern made from shapes or numbers and tell you how it would continue.

Framework objective
Describe simple patterns and relationships involving numbers or shapes; decide whether examples satisfy given conditions

Vocabulary
method, explain, pattern, order

Resources
Worksheet: Making patterns
Classroom resources: blue, red and green crayons, blue, red and green counters, shape tiles

② Making patterns

Provide the worksheet 'Making patterns'. Ask the children to complete the sheet on their own, and then compare what they have done with their partner. Discuss with them if there are other ways that they could make the pattern. Ask questions such as: *What comes next? And next?*

Teacher support
Less confident learners: Allow the children to make their patterns using counters before asking them to shade them on the activity sheet.
More confident learners: Challenge these children to make more complex patterns with the shape tiles.

Common misconception
Children do not recognise the repeats in a pattern and cannot say how it will continue.
Make a pattern using coloured counters. Put down a red counter, then a blue, then a red and so on. *What is the pattern? So what will the colour of the next counter be?* Repeat this, making different patterns. Then ask children to make their own pattern using just two colours. *What is your pattern? What colour will the next counter be?*

Probing questions
● Continue this pattern. Can you make a different pattern using the same counters?
● Can you make a pattern where the third counter is blue? Is that the only way it could be done?
● What is wrong with this pattern? Can you put it right?

Next steps
Support: Provide further opportunities for the children to copy, continue and make their own patterns, using beads, number cards, shape tiles. See also Year 1 Block B Unit 2.
Extension: Challenge the children to make more complex patterns, such as making a pattern with 3D shapes, building some on top of others. See also Year 2 Block B Unit 3.

BLOCK E

SCHOLASTIC

Activity ③

Prior learning
Children can count on from or back to zero in ones, twos, fives or tens.

Framework objective
Count on or back in ones, twos, fives and tens and use this knowledge to derive the multiples of 2, 5 and 10 to the tenth multiple

Vocabulary
count, count up to, count on from, count on to, count in ones, twos, fives, tens

Resources
Resource sheet: Self-assessment

③ Counting in ones, twos, fives and tens

Ask the children to sit in a circle. Explain that you would like them to count together. Begin by counting in ones from zero to about 30. Keep the pace sharp. Ask them to count back again. Ask them to count in ones around the circle, starting from any small number, and back again. If a child falters, say the number yourself to keep the rhythm of the count. Repeat for counting in twos, fives and tens. Note who is confident with this, and who needs more help. Decide whether to use the self-assessment sheet for the children to record their achievements and what they need to do next. They can write some of the counting patterns on the sheet.

Teacher support
Less confident learners: Limit the counting at this stage to counting in ones and twos.
More confident learners: Encourage these children to count on. For example, ask them to continue the count in twos to beyond 20.

Common misconception
Children do not know which number comes next in a count.
Practise the counting together. Ensure that children are confident with counting in ones before moving to counting in twos, and so on. Repeat the counting frequently to encourage confidence.

Probing questions
- Here is a sequence: 13, 15, 17, 19. What numbers come next?
- I say the numbers backward: 19, 17, 15, 13. What comes next?
- Count in tens from 2. Which digit changes?
- What do you notice about the ones digits when we count in fives?

Next steps
Support: Include counting in oral and mental starters so that the children become confident with counting in ones, twos, fives and tens. See also Year 1 Block E Unit 2.
Extension: Encourage the children to extend all of the counting patterns to 100. See also Year 2 Block A Unit 3.

BLOCK E

Activity ④

Prior learning
Children can find how many there are in several groups of 2, 5 or 10. They can share objects into equal groups and tell you how many there are in one group.

Framework objective
Solve practical problems that involve combining groups of 2, 5 or 10, or sharing into equal groups

Vocabulary
group, groups of, share

Resources
Resource sheet: Self-assessment
Classroom resources: counting items (cubes, counters and so on), 2p coins, paper plates

④ Groups

Provide counting materials, 2p coins, and several paper plates. Ask the children to use the coins to model the following question: *There are three 2p coins. How much money is that in total?* Discuss how they counted to find the answer. Check that they counted in twos. Now say: *The farmer has five fields. He has 15 cows. He wants the same number of cows in each field. How many cows go into each field?* Ask the children to work in pairs and to use paper plates and counting materials to help them calculate the answer. Discuss how they solved the problem. Finally, say: *There are ten plates and 20 biscuits. Share the biscuits equally so that there is the same number on each plate. How many biscuits go on each plate?* When they have completed this activity, decide whether to use the self-assessment sheet for the children to record their achievements and what they need to do next.

Teacher support
Less confident learners: Simplify the problems to groups of two.
More confident learners: Encourage these children to work mentally, counting in groups.

Common misconception
Children do not share into equal groups, nor do they count in groups of 2, 5 or 10.
Ask children to share out four cubes between two plates. *How many cubes are there in total? How many cubes are on each plate?* Repeat this for other quantities of cubes, checking that children do share these equally. Repeat for groups of 5, then 10.

Probing questions
● Count three hops of 2 along this number line. What number will you reach?
● How do you know you need to put the 15 animals into three groups? What clues are there?
● Here are 20 biscuits [counters]. Arrange them in equal rows. Can you do it differently?

Next steps
Support: Extend the children's experience to include groups of 5, then 10, as they become more confident in working with groups of 2. See also Year 1 Block E Unit 2.
Extension: Encourage the children to work mentally with grouping. Set a variety of challenges, such as: *Here are 24 cubes. Arrange them in equal rows. What equal groups can you make? What equal groups are impossible to make?* See also Year 2 Block E Unit 1.

Activity ⑤

Prior learning
Children can recall or work out doubles of numbers to at least 10. They can use doubles they know to help them work out other doubles.

Framework objective
Recall the doubles of all numbers to at least 10

Vocabulary
double

Resources
Worksheet: Doubles

⑤ Doubles

Provide the worksheet 'Doubles'. Ask the children to work with a partner to play the game. They take turns to choose a number from the grid, double it, and write the answer. The grid contains the numbers 1 to 12, so that they should use their knowledge of doubles to work out doubles that they do not know.

Teacher support
Less confident learners: Limit the range of numbers to be doubled to up to 10.
More confident learners: Extend the range of numbers to be doubled to up to 15.

Common misconception
Children have no strategy for working out an unknown double from a double they know.
Say: *We are going to find how to make double 11.* Ask children to make two towers of ten, all cubes the same colour. Ask them to add one cube in a different colour to each tower. *How many cubes are there in each tower?* Ask children to remove the extra ones. *What is double 10? What is double 1? Add these together. What is the total? So double 11 is the same as double 10 add double 1.* Repeat for up to double 15.

Probing questions
● I halve a number. The answer is 8. What is my number? Explain how you know.
● I double a number. The answer is 18. What is my number? Explain how you know.
● I know that double 10 is 20. What is double 11? How could you work it out?

Next steps
Support: Over time, include doubles beyond 10, up to about 15. Check that tje children have strategies for finding these doubles. See also Year 1 Block B Unit 3.
Extension: Challenge the children to find all the doubles to 20, and to explain how they worked these out. See also Year 2 Block B Unit 1.

BLOCK E

Activity ⑥

Prior learning
Children can find half of the water in a jug by pouring it into two glasses so that each glass has the same amount. They can tell you when the clock says half past 2. They can find a quarter of a number of objects by sharing them into four equal groups.

Framework objective
Use the vocabulary of halves and quarters in context

Vocabulary
fraction, half, halfway between, halve, quarter, whole

Resources
Worksheet: Halves and quarters
Resource sheet: Clock face
Classroom resources: jugs, water, disposable cups of the same size, teaching clock

⑥ Halves and quarters

Photocopy several copies of the resource sheet 'Clock face' onto A4 card, cut out the hands and use paper fasteners to pin them to the clock face so that each child has one. Ask the children to put up their hands to tell you the time you show on the teaching clock. Show o'clock and half-past times. Repeat, this time asking the children to set their clock faces to the times that you say. Now ask the children to take a jug of water each, and two cups. They pour the water into the two cups so that each cup has the same amount. Ask: *How much water is in this cup?* Finally, ask the children to complete the worksheet 'Halves and quarters'. They may find it helpful to fold a sheet of paper into quarters and to place their cubes onto the quarters.

Teacher support
Less confident learners: Keep telling the time to o'clock, and share into halves only.
More confident learners: Challenge these children to find other, larger, numbers that can be quartered.

Common misconception
Children do not make equal groups when finding a quarter of a quantity.
Check that children can find half of a quantity, such as six cubes, by sharing equally. Now ask them to share eight cubes equally. It will help children to see their sharing clearly if they share the cubes between four paper plates. If necessary, ask them to share by the 'one for you, one for you' method. Repeat this for finding a quarter of 12.

Probing questions
● How can I find a quarter of this strip of paper?
● There are 20 children in a classroom. Half of them are girls. How many are boys? Explain how you worked it out.
● What number is halfway between 6 and 12? How did you work it out?

Next steps
Support: Extend the children's work with time using, for example, oral and mental starters which include reading clocks for half past. Extend sharing quantities to finding quarters. Provide paper plates to help the children to share the cubes equally. See also Year 1 Block E Unit 2.
Extension: Set challenges, such as: *Find all the numbers between 20 and 40 which can be quartered.* See also Year 2 Block E Unit 1.

Units 1, 2 & 3 ◻ Periodic assessment

These activities can be used at the end of this block to assess those children that you think have achieved the objectives.

Adding and subtracting

Objective
Use the vocabulary related to addition and subtraction and symbols to describe and record addition and subtraction number sentences

Assessment focus
Level 1: Draw simple conclusions from their work, e.g. with support explain numbers and calculations, how many altogether, how many used or hidden, how many left, how many each, etc. Record their work, e.g. record their work with objects, pictures or diagrams; begin to use the symbols '+' and '=' to record additions.
Foundation stage profile scale points: In practical activities and discussion, begins to use the vocabulary involved in adding and subtracting

Learning outcomes
● I can describe an addition or subtraction using mathematical words (in a practical context).
● I can record an addition or subtraction number sentence and tell you what it means.

There are two activities for this objective, which are suitable for use at the end of Unit 1 and Unit 2 respectively.

1. Working with a group of children, ask them to solve the word problems on the worksheet 'Adding and subtracting (1)'. Note which children can calculate mentally and which need to use practical materials such as cubes or number lines. Ask the children to explain the strategies that they used and to express the problem's solution in words, as a number sentence. Decide whether to use the self-assessment sheet for the children to record their achievements and what they need to do next. They can draw two of the sets and write the totals on the sheet.
2. Ask the children to write the number sentences for the word problems on the worksheet 'Adding and subtracting (2)'. Check that they can explain the number sentence and say what it means.

Combining groups, sharing and grouping

Objective
Solve practical problems that involve combining groups of 2, 5 or 10, or sharing into equal groups

Assessment focus
Level 1: Order numbers to 10; begin to count in twos. Begin to use the fraction, one-half, e.g. halve an even number of objects

Learning outcomes
● I can share objects into equal groups and work out how many in one group.
● I can find how many there are in several groups of 2, 5 or 10.
● I can share objects into equal groups and tell you how many there are in one group.

Sharing: Work with a group of about six children. Provide cubes and paper plates and the self-assessment sheet. The children can draw the results of their sharing on the sheet. Say: *Share out eight cubes between two plates. How many cubes are there on one plate? Now share out ten cubes between five plates. How many cubes on one plate?* Continue for sharing by 2, 5 and 10, keeping the total number of cubes to up to 20.

(continued overleaf)

Combining groups, sharing and grouping (continued)

Foundation stage profile scale points: Uses developing mathematical ideas and methods to solve practical problems

2p, 5p and 10p: Provide the children with coins and a paper plate. Say: *Put out three 2p coins. How much money is that?* Check that the children count in twos to find the answer or 'know' it. Repeat for other values for 2p, such as six 2p coins. Repeat this for 5p coins, then 10p coins. Check how the children calculate the totals. Decide whether to use the self-assessment sheet for the children to record their achievements and what they need to do next. They can record some of their totals on the sheet.

Equal groups: Provide 20 counters. Ask the children to find a way to put the counters into equal groups. They can arrange their counters into equal rows, like an array. Ask: *How many counters are there in each row? How many rows are there?* Ask the children to repeat this, and find a different way to make equal rows. They can record their arrays on the self-assessment sheet.

Patterns

Objective
Describe simple patterns and relationships involving numbers or shapes; decide whether examples satisfy given conditions

Assessment focus
Level 1: Recognise and use a simple pattern or relationship, e.g. with support copy and continue a simple pattern of objects, shapes or numbers
Foundation stage profile scale points: Talks about, recognises and recreates simple patterns

Learning outcome
● I can describe a pattern made from shapes or numbers and tell you how it would continue.

Provide the worksheet 'Patterns', some shape tiles and some counters in three different colours. Ask the children to use the shape tiles and counters to make the patterns illustrated on the worksheet, and then to continue them. Observe how they go about the task, and whether they are confident in finding the pattern sequence and can continue it.

Name	Date

Adding and subtracting (1)

Answer these word problems.

1. There are 4 camels at the zoo.
The zoo keeper buys 3 more camels.
How many camels are there altogether?

_____

2. There are 8 penguins in the pool.
2 penguins leave the pool.
How many penguins are left in the pool?

_____

3. There are 5 parrots and 3 toucans.
How many birds is that in total?

_____

4. There are 9 lions.
3 of the lions are cubs.
How many lions are not cubs?

_____

How easy?

Red
Amber
Green

How do you think you have done?

_____

_____

BLOCK E

Name   Date

Adding and subtracting (2)

Write a number sentence for each of these word problems. Then write the answer.

1. There are 4 red flowers and 3 blue flowers.
How many flowers are there altogether?

_____

2. 8 butterflies are in the bush.
3 butterflies fly away.
How many butterflies are there now?

_____

3. 10 ants walk on the path.
3 of the ants crawl into a hole.
How many ants are there on the path?

_____

4. There are 9 flower pots on the ground.
Anna picks up 4 flowerpots.
How many flowerpots are left on the ground?

_____

How easy?

Red
Amber
Green

How do you think you have done?

_____

_____

BLOCK E

Name	Date

Patterns

You will need some shape tiles and some counters in three different colours.

1. You need counters in two different colours.
- Make this pattern with your counters:

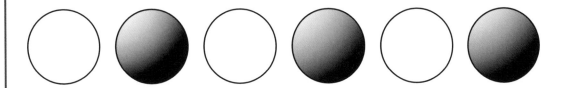

- Use your counters to continue the pattern.

2. Now use some shape tiles.
- Copy this pattern:

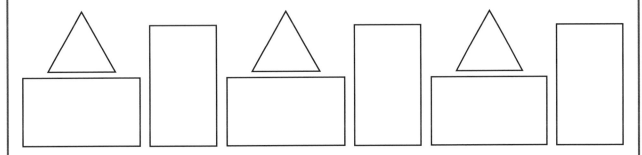

- Use your shape tiles to continue the pattern.

3. Use three different colours of counters.
- Make your own pattern.
- Ask a partner to continue your pattern.

How easy?

Red
Amber
Green

How do you think you have done?

_____

_____

BLOCK E

Transitional assessment

Activity	Type	Level	Description
1.1	Single-level written assessment	1	20-minute formal test paper covering objectives from all Strands of the Framework at Level 1
1.2	Single-level written assessment	1	20-minute formal test paper covering objectives from all Strands of the Framework at Level 1
1.3	Single-level written assessment	1	20-minute formal test paper covering objectives from all Strands of the Framework at Level 1
1.4	Single-level oral and practical assessment	1	Oral paper administered to groups of up to four children, covering objectives from all Strands of the Framework at Level 1
1.5	Single-level oral and practical assessment	1	Oral paper administered to groups of up to four children, covering objectives from all Strands of the Framework at Level 1
2.1	Single-level written assessment	2	30-minute formal test paper covering objectives from all Strands of the Framework at Level 2
2.2	Single-level written assessment	2	30-minute formal test paper covering objectives from all Strands of the Framework at Level 2
2.3	Single-level written assessment	2	30-minute formal test paper covering objectives from all Strands of the Framework at Level 2
2.4	Single-level oral assessment	2	Approximately 5-minute oral paper covering objectives from all Strands of the Framework at Level 2
2.5	Single-level oral assessment	2	Approximately 5-minute oral paper covering objectives from all Strands of the Framework at Level 2

TRANSITIONAL

Written test instructions

Allow 20 minutes for each paper at Level 1 and 30 minutes for each paper at Level 2.

Children should work so that they cannot see each other's work.

Do not explain questions or read numbers to the children.

For Level 1, teachers should read the questions aloud to the children. For Level 2, they may choose to read the questions aloud if they feel it is appropriate.

The test may be administered to groups of children or to the whole class.

The total marks available for each paper are given in the mark scheme.

Say to the children:

Here are some questions (I am going to read some questions) for you to answer.
For some questions you will write your answer in a box. [Show example.]
For some questions you may need to draw lines or rings to show your answer.
[Show example.]
If you make a mistake, you should cross it out (or rub it out neatly) and write your answer clearly.
You may use spaces on the paper to do any working out that may help you.
Try to work out the answer to each question before going on to the next one.
If you can't answer a question, move on to the next one - it may be easier.

Equipment for each child

Level 1: pencil, eraser (or children may cross out mistakes), interlocking cubes

Level 2: pencil, eraser (or children may cross out mistakes), a 30cm ruler (marked in millimetres), structured apparatus consisting of tens and units (for example, base 10 equipment, interlocking cubes), mirror, tracing paper

Oral test instructions

Level 1: This oral and practical assessment can be administered to groups of up to four children. Read the questions to the children. Allow sufficient time for a child to work out an answer. Children respond orally. 1 mark per question: 10 marks total. Separate teacher resources are listed for each paper.

Level 2: Read questions to the children no more than twice. Allow five seconds for each answer. Children record their answers on paper (necessary equipment: pencil, eraser (or children may cross out mistakes), 30cm ruler). 1 mark per question: 15 marks total. Separate teacher resources are listed for each paper.

Levelling the children

Add together the marks from an oral test and a written test.

Level 1		Level 2	
Below Level 1	0 – 10 marks	Below Level 2	0 – 15 marks
Low Level 1	11 – 14 marks	Low Level 2	16 – 22 marks
Secure Level 1	15 – 19 marks	Secure Level 2	22 – 28 marks
High Level 1	20 – 24 marks	High Level 2	28 – 36 marks

When awarding an end-of-year Teacher Assessment Level, teachers also need to consider a child's performance on Periodic and Day-to-Day Assessments.

TRANSITIONAL

Mathematics: making a level judgement

Use these steps to formalise your assessments of pupils' mathematics into level judgements.

You will need
- evidence of the pupil's mathematics that shows most independence, for example from work in other subjects as well as in mathematics lessons
- other evidence about the pupil as a mathematician, for example notes on plans, the pupil's own reflections, your own recollections of classroom interactions, oral answers given during mental starters
- a copy of the assessment guidelines for the level borderline that is your starting point.

Step 1: Making best-fit judgements
Within each assessment focus, draw on the pupil's work and other evidence including what you know about the pupil's mathematics. Use the criteria in the assessment guidelines to decide which level provides the best fit.

Step 2: Work through Ma2 Number
Begin with the assessment guidelines for Ma2 Number.

Look at the criteria within each AF. Decide which level describes the pupil best.

Record the level for each AF in the appropriate box.

Record 'insufficient evidence' (IE) if you do not know enough about this aspect of the pupil's mathematics to make a judgement. This has implications for planning.

If you feel the pupil is operating below the level, check the criteria on the assessment guidelines for the level below.

Step 3: Making an overall level judgement for Ma2 Number
Now make your level decision for Ma2 Number.

- Your AF judgements give an impression of the best-fit level for Ma2.
- Read the complete level descriptions for both levels to confirm your impression of the best-fit level for Ma2

Decide whether the level is Low, Secure or High. Do this by thinking about what the pupil demonstrates:
- how much of the level
- how consistently
- how independently
- in what range of contexts.

Tick the relevant Low, Secure or High box for the level.

Step 4: Repeat the process for Ma3, Ma4 and then Ma1
For the Ma1 judgement, consider how the pupil uses and applies the mathematics of Ma2, Ma3 and Ma4.

APP 🔲 Self-assessment sheet

Name _____   Date _____

Activity name _____

Objective:
Learning outcome:
Comments:

Self-assessment

How well did you do this? _____

_____

_____

_____

What do you still need to do? _____

_____

_____

_____

How easy?

Red

Amber

Green

How do you think you have done?

_____

_____

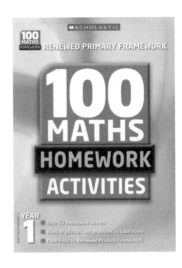

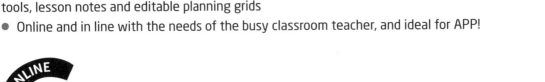